Health&Fitness

10-MINUTE MINDFULNESS

Words Eve Boggenpoel
Images iStock

Editor Mary Comber
Art Director Lucy Pinto
Chief Sub-editor Sheila Reid

Publisher Steven O'Hara
Publishing Director Dan Savage
Marketing Manager Charlotte Park
Commercial Director Nigel Hole

Printed by William Gibbons and Sons, Wolverhampton

MORTONS
MEDIA GROUP LTD

Published by Mortons Media Group Ltd,
Media Centre, Morton Way,
Horncastle, LN9 6JR
01507 529529

MAG**BOOK**

Contents

p90

p34

CONTENTS

p80

Welcome

Thank you for choosing this book. As you'll discover over the following pages, being mindful doesn't always involve formal exercises or meditations. In fact, you may already be practising mindfulness without realising it. When you catch the scent of blossom on a spring day and pause to trace its origin, you're being mindful. When you hesitate before answering the phone and ask yourself if you really need to take the call, you're being mindful. When you stop long enough to notice your breath, you're being mindful.

One of the beauties of mindfulness is that it brings you closer to yourself and enables you to reach towards where you want to be. In fact, they are often the same thing. I have been meditating for many years, and consistently find it takes me to a place beyond thought, a place that enables me to draw on a rich source of wisdom not influenced by insecurities, prejudice or expectation. This deeply intuitive self-contact can guide you through your day-to-day challenges but also give you a sense of direction and purpose that may otherwise elude you. When I am seeking answers to a difficulty I'm facing or looking for more fulfilment in my life, before searching for a practical solution, I often ask myself: 'What really matters? What is the truth? What can I trust?'

Whatever drew you to this book, I hope that living more mindfully supports you in answering the important questions in your life and gives you tools to help you live it in a more meaningful way.

Eve Boggenpoel, author *10-minute Mindfulness*

THE AUTHOR

Eve Boggenpoel has been practising meditation for more than 25 years, initially under the guidance of teachers Sophie Johnson and Hilmar Schönauer. As a yoga teacher and qualified homeopath, she has shared mindfulness and meditation practices with clients and students for many years. As a health journalist she has written for titles including *Health & Fitness*, *Top Santé*, *Natural Health*, and *Women's Running* and is the author of two books on yoga. *10-minute Mindfulness* brings together her intuitive understanding of healing and a deep appreciation of the power of meditation in transforming lives.

HOW TO USE
this book

Keen to begin your mindfulness journey? Read this introduction
to ensure you get the most out of this guide

1. DISCOVER MINDFULNESS

Find out just what mindfulness is, how
it can benefit you and why it works.
Discover the scientifically-proven benefits
of being more mindful and how it can
actually change the structure of your
brain and bring you a greater sense of
calm and purpose.

2. FIRST STEPS

Make a start with meditation using these
simple practices. Deepen your breathing
by gently receiving the in-breath and
finding calm release on the out-breath.
Use a counting technique to help you
observe the movement of your thoughts,
and learn to meditate on a single object
with an ancient yoga technique.

P66

P118

3. ON THE GO

Once you've gathered some experience in tuning into your body and observing your thoughts and emotions, learn how to extend these skills into other activities such as mindful walking. Discover how you can use the rhythm of your footsteps to help you return to the present moment and stay more grounded.

4. MOMENT BY MOMENT

Dip into these pages when you want inspiration for how to use mindfulness in everyday situations. Whether you're on your own, at work or with a group of friends, be grateful; learn how to be your own best friend; uncover your stress triggers and discover what it feels like to be a child again.

✳
PART ONE:
THE BASICS

If you're not exactly sure what being mindful involves, this is the place to start. Here, you'll learn the history and main concepts of mindfulness, and get an idea of how your life might look after you learn to live more fully in the moment. Discover the ways mindfulness is used by its many advocates – from celebrities to professors – and learn how it can benefit you, too. Take the quiz on p18 to become aware of the many areas of life that mindfulness can impact on, then find out how being more present can enhance your memory, help you lose weight and even improve your sex life.

By being fully present... you're able to inhabit the moment in a way that brings a wealth of benefits, including reduced feelings of stress and anxiety, better communication and increased concentration

WHAT IS
mindfulness?

By emptying your mind and
being in the present moment,
you can reap a wealth of benefits

Mindfulness has become a serious
buzzword in recent years – do a
Google search and you'll get almost
63 million results! From health to
education, business and personal
wellbeing, mindfulness is seen in almost every walk of life.
The NHS prescribes it to patients experiencing stress and
depression, offering staff training on the techniques, too;
Harvard Business School includes its principles in its leadership
programmes; and Google and eBay are just two of the
companies that have dedicated rooms for staff to practise
mindfulness meditation in work time. So what is mindfulness,
and how did it all begin?

ORIGINS

While it has its roots in Buddhism,
mindfulness as we know it today with
its focus on being fully present in the
current moment was developed by the
scientist, Jon Kabat-Zinn, founder of the
world-renowned Mindfulness-Based
Stress Reduction Clinic and the Center
for Mindfulness in Medicine, Health
Care and Society in the US and now
the emeritus Professor of Medicine
at the University of Massachusetts
Medical School.

In the 1970s he adapted Buddhist
meditation techniques to help people
with chronic illnesses manage their
conditions, inspired by a study
he conducted on patients with
psoriasis. After being taught to
meditate while receiving ultra-violet
light treatment, the participants'
skin conditions cleared up at four
times the rate of the non-meditators,
all because they learnt to focus on
the present moment.

CREATING CLARITY

If you've looked round for that half-eaten sandwich only to find you've finished it, or walked to the end of your road and wondered if you double locked the front door you'll know what it's like to live on auto pilot. For many of us it's the norm. We're so preoccupied with our thoughts, catching up on a stream of unanswered emails or trying to spend time with friends and family at the weekend and still have time to shop that – understandably – we tend to think in terms of the number of tasks we get through in a day rather than the quality of their experience. When was the last time you watched a sunset or smelled a flower? And how long is it since you simply enjoyed a cup of tea – no checking your mobile or watching TV?

As well as allowing you to deeply appreciate the smaller moments in life, being more mindful can also bring a sense of calm and ease to the more challenging ones. By being fully present, aware of your thoughts, emotions and bodily sensations, you're able to inhabit the moment in a way that brings a wealth of benefits, including reduced feelings of stress and anxiety, a more balanced response to difficult situations, better communication, more satisfying relationships and increased focus and concentration. It's even been shown to enhance your immune system.

'Mindfulness is awareness, cultivated by paying attention in a sustained and particular way; on purpose, in the present moment, and non-judgmentally, in the service of self-understanding and wisdom,' says Kabat-Zinn. 'This kind of attention nurtures greater awareness, clarity and acceptance of present-moment reality. It wakes us up to the fact that our lives unfold only in moments. If we're not fully present for many of those moments, we may not only miss what is most valuable in our lives but also fail to realise

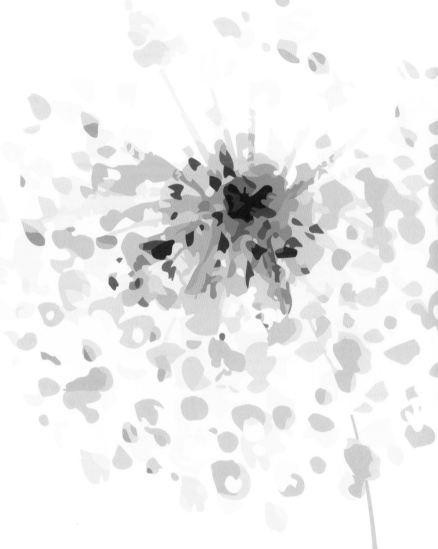

DEVELOPING MINDFULNESS

Mindfulness doesn't mean you have to sit for hours in lotus position while you try to empty your mind of thoughts. Essentially, there are two main ways to develop mindfulness – formally, using guided meditations or practising stand-alone techniques such as the body scan (p46) or eating a raisin exercise (p44); or informally, by incorporating mindfulness skills into your daily life (p28). Essentially, you are guiding your attention and energy in a way that enables you to alter, ideally for the better, the quality of your experience, in turn becoming more fully aware of your humanity and your relationship to others.

Emma Watson, actress, and yoga and meditation teacher

The actress turned to yoga and meditation to anchor her busy lifestyle. 'I needed to find a way to always feel safe and at home within myself. I started being interested in meditation in a literary way, but I realised reading books wasn't enough, you have to practise for it to work. So I started it, and I love it, it helps me a lot.'

Angelina Jolie, actress, filmaker and humanitarian

The ambassador for UN refugee agency UNHCR has found a way to be mindful in everyday life, informal mindfulness, as it's known. 'I find meditation in sitting on the floor with the kids colouring for an hour, or going on the trampoline.'

the richness and depth of our possibilities for growth and transformation.'

BRAIN BENEFITS

And it's not just about feeling good – there are a whole host of benefits. Recent research by Harvard University shows that the brain can create new grey matter in the hippocampus, an area involved with learning and memory. The study also showed an increase in areas associated with self-awarenss and compassion.

Harvard Medical School pyschology instructor and senior study author Sara Lazar explains: 'Although meditation is associated with a sense of peacefulness and physical relaxation, practitioners have long claimed that meditation also provides cognitive and psychological benefits that persist throughout the day. This study demonstrates that changes in brain structure may underlie some of these reported improvements and that people are not just feeling better because they are spending time relaxing.'

One of the reasons mindfulness works is because it opens up a space between what happens to you and how you react. All too often, we react unconsciously to situations, unaware of the relationship between our thoughts, feelings and actions. When you've been overlooked yet again for a job promotion it's easy to slip into old patterns. If your childhood efforts weren't valued by parents or teachers, it's no surprise if, as an adult, you feel a sense of shame or self-righteous anger when similarly treated. Integrative counsellor and psychotherapist Anna McNally refers to it as time travelling – reacting to a present situation from a mindset more appropriate to a past experience. What mindfulness training does is give you the space to be fully present in the moment, so you can choose how you act in a manner appropriate to the situation.

IS IT FOR ME?

Many myths surround meditation practices. Here are some of the common concerns about mindfulness techniques.

'I'M NOT RELIGIOUS'

Although you'll be meditating, possibly even following Buddhist practices, mindfulness is completely secular, and doesn't require any religious or spiritual beliefs. It won't turn you into a tree hugger either! On the contrary, all mindfulness will do is bring you closer to who you really are.

'I CAN'T EMPTY MY MIND'

Being mindful isn't about trying to empty your mind of all its thoughts. It's the opposite, encouraging you to become aware of your thoughts, along with your feelings and bodily sensations. Once you have this awareness, you can choose which thoughts you want to keep and which you can let go.

'I DON'T WANT TO BECOME TOO RELAXED'

Rather than make you lethargic, practising mindfulness can sharpen your mind and make you more focused. Instead of being distracted or so busy you don't complete anything, mindfulness helps centre you and keep you on track.

Oprah Winfrey, actress, producer and media proprietor

As a talk show host, Oprah has interviewed mindfulness giants from Jon Kabat-Zinn to Zen buddhist monk, Thich Naht Hahn, but she has her own views on the subject too. 'Meditate. Breathe consciously. Listen. Pay attention. Treasure every moment. Make the connection. Let go. And remind yourself that this very moment is the only one you know you have for sure.'

BE HERE NOW

MIND OVER MATTER

Confused about the different types of mindfulness? Here are the basic forms you'll meet on your mindfulness journey.

BUDDHIST MINDFULNESS

Mindfulness in Buddhism is one of the teachings that form the Eightfold path, a guide to freedom from suffering. After his own 'enlightenment', the Buddha spoke of the Four Foundations of Mindfulness: Mindfulness of body, Mindfulness of feelings, Mindfulness of mind and Mindfulness of Dharma (the natural law of things). As you go through this book, you'll see how these four areas form the foundation of mindfulness techniques we still use today, 2,500 years later. For example, the vipassana meditation from the oldest living Buddhist tradition, Theravada, involves focusing your attention on the breath as a way to cultivate awareness.

MINDFULNESS-BASED STRESS REDUCTION (MBSR)

The father of modern day mindfulness is a formal eight-week programme created by Jon Kabat-Zinn in 1979, which has also been produced in a self-help workbook format. It helps you become aware of your habitual reactions to situations and teaches you how to break the cycle in order to give yourself greater freedom of choice in how you experience yourself and others. Research shows MBSR is enormously helpful for people with chronic pain, hypertension, heart disease, cancer, and gastrointestinal disorders, as well as anxiety and panic.

MINDFULNESS-BASED COGNITIVE THERAPY (MBCT)

Developed by University of Toronto professor of psychology Zindel Segal, emeritus Professor of Clinical Psychology Mark Williams and research scientist John Teasdale, MBCT combines breathing exercises, meditation and stretching with elements of cognitive therapy. In the 1990s, research by Teasdale and psychologist Philip Barnard discovered the two main modes of the mind – 'doing' and 'being'. 'Doing' mind is goal-oriented, while 'being' mind accepts what is. It's this latter mode that leads to lasting emotional changes, and MBCT has been developed to support people who experience repeated bouts of depression.

HOW *mindful* ARE YOU?

Do you live in the moment or is your mind distracted? Answer the questions on the next page to see whether you could benefit from mindfulness training

How often are you aware of **being fully in the present moment?** With pressures on us to meet work, family and social commitments, it's all too easy to multitask our way through the day, thinking about how we could have handled that situation at the office differently, planning what we're going to eat in the evening or simply wishing we were somewhere else than right here, right now. And when we feel this way, either consciously or subconsciously, we travel with our minds, thinking our way out of the present moment. And it soon shows – the tell-tale symptoms of a distracted mind can start almost as soon as we begin the day, 'Where did I put my train pass?' or 'Did I remember to double lock the front door?'. Sometimes, it's even 'I can't remember if I put deodorant on!' If you're unsure how mindfulness training could work for you, take a look at the following questions and see how often they apply to your life.

BODY AWARENESS

1. Do you often engage in unconscious snacking/comfort eating?

2. Would you like to improve your fitness?

3. Are you sometimes surprised to realise that your breathing has become more shallow or your heart is beating faster?

4. Have you ever found a bruise on your leg and not recalled when you got it?

5. Would you like to lose weight?

6. If you were to tune into your body right now, would you become aware of any muscular tension?

7. Do you wait until you feel really thirsty before you have a drink of water?

8. Is your sex life less satisfying than you'd like it to be?

9. Do you ever continue eating beyond the point of feeling full?

MIND MATTERS

1. Are you a multitasker?

2. Do you struggle with decision making?

3. Is it sometimes difficult for you to express your thoughts precisely?

4. When you're eating, do you like to read, work or watch TV?

5. Does your mind ever wander when you're in a meeting or a colleague is talking to you?

6. Are you an impulse shopper?

7. Do you rush from place to place without being aware of your surroundings?

8. When you're working, commuting or doing the housework, are you often thinking about something else you'd rather be doing?

9. Do you often go over past experiences in your mind?

EMOTIONAL INTELLIGENCE

1. When someone asks you what you're feeling, do you struggle to easily identify your emotions?

2. Are there certain feelings you think you shouldn't have?

3. Do you sometimes distract yourself to avoid experiencing unpleasant emotions?

4. Is it challenging for you to spend a lot of time on your own?

5. Would you like to have more control over how you feel?

6. Will you often put other people's wishes before your own, even if it means you'll suffer in some way?

7. Does it occasionally take a day or two for you to react to an event or situation?

8. Are you sometimes out of touch with your emotional needs?

9. Would you like to have greater self-confidence?

If you can relate to these questions, then mindfulness could make a big difference to your life. In fact, the more 'yes' answers you gave, the greater the results you'll see from incorporating the ideas in this book into your life. Read on to find out how you can enrich your daily experience and create the life you want through the practice of mindfulness.

THE BENEFITS OF
mindfulness

Living in the moment increases your mental and physical wellbeing. We show you how

So often in our lives we're anywhere but in this present moment. Even in the middle of cooking supper, going for a run or writing an email, part of our attention is trying not to forget about a phone call we promised to make or wondering why our best friend/partner was so irritable yesterday. Or, perhaps we're feeding our self-critical mind, saying things such as, 'I'll never get the job I want', or 'If only I was prettier, slimmer'. And while our thoughts often need further attention, acknowledging them (writing them down, if necessary) and returning to a state of mindfulness in the present can bring a host of benefits.

Did you know that being mindful can ease depression and boost self-esteem? Or aid decision-making and rebuild your brain? It can help you manage chronic illness and cope with long-term pain; it enhances relationships, helps you focus on your goals and enables you to deal with emotions better. And, you don't need to be anywhere else than where you already are.

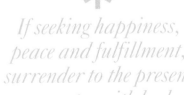

If seeking happiness, peace and fulfillment, surrender to the present moment – with body, emotions and mind

If you want to see minfulness in action, consider the behaviour of cats. When the sun comes out they'll slink over to the warmest patch of grass and bask in the pleasure of their own body. Watch them stretch out after a nap and they'll luxuriate in the sensation. Stroke their tummy and they'll purr to their heart's content; stop, and the moment is over.

You can see a similar pattern in young children at play. They're not thinking of yesterday's game, they're absorbed in their current experience. If they get upset they'll sit on your lap and cry. Once they finish, they'll laugh and run around.

If you're seeking happiness, peace and fulfilment, the key is to surrender to the present moment – with your body, emotions and mind. A Harvard University study found that happiness wasn't as much related to the activity you're doing, but to your thoughts about the activity at the time – that is, you're happiest when your mind is on what you're doing. Turn over, to discover some of the other ways mindfulness can increase your sense of wellbeing.

1. LOVE YOUR BODY

Research shows even a brief period of meditation focusing on self-compassion – such as the loving kindness meditation (p60) – can improve your relationship to your body. In a three-week trial, researchers found participants who were given meditation training had significantly greater reduction in body dissatisfaction and self-worth based on appearance, and greater gains in self-compassion and body appreciation compared with a control group. What's more, the improvements remained when the participants were assessed three months later.

2 Boost your brain

When you're under pressure at work, rather than compiling yet another to-do list that will send your stress levels soaring, take time out to meditate. Doing just four sessions of mindfulness training has been shown to improve visual processing, working memory and executive functioning of the brain (the processes involved in managing oneself and one's resources to achieve a goal). A study published in *Consciousness and Cognition* journal gave participants an audio book to listen to and found that the group who received mindfulness meditation training showed improved cognitive abilities, along with reduced fatigue and anxiety, when compared with the control group. Set aside some space for mindfulness before and during your next big work project.

3. LOSE THAT EXCESS WEIGHT (AT LAST!)

There's good evidence that mindful eating strategies can have an influence on what you eat. In particular, focusing on the sensory properties of food while eating – for example its taste, texture, look and smell – can stop you reaching for high-calorie snacks later in the day. In a review of studies on mindfulness interventions for weight loss, among eight randomised controlled trials published in peer-reviewed journals, six showed significant weight loss among participants. Other mindful strategies, such as accepting your thoughts and feelings, can help reduce the need for emotional eating, and you won't feel you have to give up because you accept that it's all right to slip up.

4 Banish distractions

Do you struggle to complete work assignments on schedule? Say goodbye to distracting thoughts with meditation. Research from Harvard Medical School shows that an eight-week mindfulness programme helps to modulate the alpha rhythm in your brain. Particularly active in cells that process sight, sound and touch in the cortex, the brain's outermost layer, the alpha rhythm helps to suppress distracting sensations that pull you away from the task at hand. After they had completed their mindfulness training, participants 'made faster and significantly more pronounced attention-based adjustments to the alpha rhythm than those in the control group,' say the researchers.

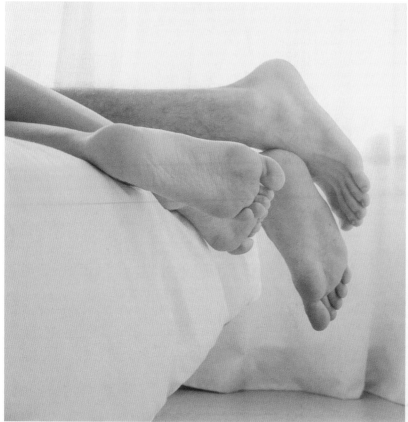

6 Improve your sex life

Do you long for greater intimacy with your partner? Perhaps you wish they would touch you in a certain way, or maybe you feel hesitant about expressing your needs? It's quite common to have an inner dialogue going on while you're making love – which your partner has no idea about! If you're absorbed in your thoughts and not the experience of your body, your capacity to enjoy sex is greatly reduced. By dropping your attention from your head and consciously choosing to be fully present in your body, you'll be much more open to receiving the quality of your partner's touch and fully experiencing the sensations it arouses in you. You may even discover the intimacy you long for was there all the time.

5 Lift depression

Mindfulness-based cognitive therapy (MBCT) includes mindfulness exercises, yoga, body awareness and daily practices such as housework or cleaning your teeth with full attention, moment by moment. Research by Oxford University, published in *The Lancet*, shows that MBCT is as effective as medication for preventing repeat bouts of depression, and the more challenging the participants' childhood experiences, the more effective it is. 'MBCT helps them to recognise what's happening, engage with it in a different way and respond to it with equanimity and compassion,' says the study's lead author Professor Williem Kuylen.

7. BEAT PAIN

A shocking 28 million of people in the UK suffer from chronic pain – almost half the population (43 per cent). And it's not just the elderly, more than a third of sufferers are under 75. Chronic pain is defined as pain that continues for more than three months, so if that includes you, you'll know how debilitating it can be. The good news? A study by the University of Washington found an eight-week mindfulness-based stress reduction (MBSR) programme significantly improved pain levels and functional ability – and they were still present six and 12 months after completion of the course.

8. EASE SYMPTOMS OF CHRONIC ILLNESS

Long-term illness is especially debilitating. But mindfulness has been shown to help make conditions more manageable, even illnesses as serious as cancer. A study by the University of Calgary found a seven-week programme of MBSR had positive benefits for a group of cancer outpatients. After the completion of the 90-minute weekly meditation classes, the patients had a 31 per cent reduction in symptoms of stress, and 65 per cent fewer mood disturbances. What's more, they also experienced less cardiopulmonary and gastrointestinal symptoms, and less emotional irritability, depression and cognitive disorganisation.

Online programmes are effective too. The eCALM trial offered patients mindfulness-based cancer recovery (MBCR), a 'real-time' group psychosocial programme, consisting of eight two-hour online classes and a six-hour retreat. Patients reported improved mood and stress reduction. They also had a calmer response to difficult experiences and had more energy.

9 *Enhance communication*

How often do you know exactly what you'd like to say to someone – the day after you had the conversation? When you're in the middle of a conversation – especially one that's emotionally charged or taking place while your attention is being pulled in another direction – it's not always easy to be in touch with the truth of what you're feeling, let alone find the best way of expressing it. Maybe you're speaking to someone who's hypersensitive and you know you need to tread carefully around them. Or perhaps it's a subject that you feel strongly about, but you don't yet know how best to contain your feelings and still get your point across in a clear, lucid way.

Being in a mindful state helps you manage your feelings without losing sight of them, and enables you to maintain the clarity of thought you need to contact your inner self and then get your point over in a way that respects both parties. If you struggle with this, turn to p94 for more on skillful communication using mindfulness.

✳

PART TWO:
MINDFUL
EXERCISES

*In this section of the book, you'll
learn everything from how to sit
when you meditate to creating a
tailor-made, one-day retreat.
Learn the key introductory
exercises you need to become
familiar with mindfulness
techniques, then put what you've
understood into practice as you
find out how to apply
mindfulness to specific situations
such as meeting your goals or
managing stress. First, discover
how your breath not only soothes
and calms you, but also brings
you instantly back to the present
moment. Then, learn what you
need to begin your mindful
journey and how to connect with
the community of like-minded
people travelling with you.*

MAKING A START

breathe well

Connecting with your breath
will always bring you back
to the present moment

**he simplest way
to bring more
mindfulness into
your life is by
observing your
breath.** It's your direct link with the
present moment and brings you back
to yourself. Donna Farhi, author of *The
Breathing Book*, points out that the
process of breathing is so inseparable
from who we deeply are, it has even
permeated our language – 'to inspire' is
both to inhale and to touch someone's
heart; in Japanese, 'Ki' means both
air and spirit; in Chinese the three
characters for breath, 'tsi', translate as
'of the conscious self or heart'. So what
happens if we don't breathe as well as
we could?

Most of the time, we are unaware of how we breathe. Whether from stress, inattention or simply habit, rather than nourishing ourselves with deep, full breaths, we subconsciously choose to breathe too fast, too shallow or just take quick, superficial 'gasps' into the top of our chest. This, in turn, means we're not only losing out on a host of physiological benefits – deep breathing has been shown to ease headaches, high blood pressure, asthma and anxiety – but we're also less aware of what we are feeling in the moment. Our breath brings us back to our true selves. It teaches us to be more mindful.

In order to breathe well, it helps to have a little understanding of breathing anatomy. The main muscle that controls your breath is the diaphragm. It's a dome-shaped muscle that covers the entire floor of your chest cavity. Think of it as an umbrella that flattens and opens out as you breathe in, closes inwards and upwards as you breath out. If you place your hands on your ribs, it's the diaphragm that causes them to expand as you inhale and contract again as you exhale. To breathe fully and deeply, it's important to allow your diaphragm to expand in all directions, to the front, back and sides.

BREATHING WITH YOUR *whole body*

This exercise will help you become more familiar with your own breathing pattern, and teach you how to expand your breath at will, so you can switch to deeper breathing wherever you are and whatever situation you're in. Switch off all distractions, make sure you'll be warm enough and allow yourself 15 to 20 minutes.

Direct your breath, first filling your abdomen, then your ribs and finally your upper chest… as you exhale, reverse the process

Lie on your back, gently close your eyes and take a moment to let your mind settle. Breathing in through your nose, exhale through your mouth with an audible sigh, releasing any tension in your body on your out-breath. Do this twice more, letting go of any thoughts as you exhale, and surrendering your body into the floor.

Without trying to change anything, notice how you are breathing, becoming aware of the movements in your body as you breathe. Does your lower belly rise and fall? Can you sense your ribs expanding and contracting? Maybe you feel your back compress against the floor as you inhale.

After a few moments, place your hands on your lower belly, with your fingertips touching and the heels of your hands out to the sides, and see if you can notice it rising as you inhale and gently falling as you exhale.

Gently slide your hands to rest on your side ribs. Can you sense any movement beneath your hands?

✿ Finally, slide to your upper chest.
Can you feel any micro movement
beneath your fingers? Your lungs reach
right up to your clavicle, but we rarely
use their full capacity.

✿ See if you can direct your breath,
first filling your abdomen, then your
ribs and finally your upper chest, as if
you were filling a vase with water – first
the base, then the middle and finally the
neck. As you exhale, reverse the
process, emptying from your chest, then
your ribs and finally your belly.

✿ Like the vase, your diaphragm
and lungs are three-dimensional,
so allow your breath to travel to the
back and sides of your body as well
as the front.

✿ Continue in your own rhythm for a
few breaths, then gently let your
breathing return to normal.

✳ KEEP A BREATHING JOURNAL

Noticing how you breathe
throughout the day will help
transform your relationship with
your breath, making it easier to
sink into a deeper, more mindful
breathing at will. Simply check in
three times a day, bringing your
awareness to your breath and
noticing how it is. Are you taking
short, shallow breaths, or are
you breathing deeply and evenly
into your belly? Where are you
breathing from – your abdomen
or your chest? Perhaps you've
even been holding your breath.

After a week or so, read back
over your entries and notice if a
pattern has emerged. Maybe you

tend to hold your breath when
you speak to your boss, or you
only really breathe evenly and
fully when you're alone. Notice in
which situations you find yourself
taking shallow breaths. When do
you take deep, easeful breaths,
and how does that make you feel?

Often, simply bringing your
attention to your breath opens
the door to change. When you
notice your breath has become
fast, shallow or even held, if you
can, take a few moments out to
allow any tension in your jaw,
neck, shoulders and upper body
to release, then invite the breath
deeper into your belly.

WHAT *you* NEED

Use accessories, apps and online
training to help you get into
a meditative state

The beauty of mindfulness exercises is that all you need is yourself. That said, our busy, tech-filled lives bombard us with information from dawn to dusk, and our minds are often so stimulated it's hard to switch them off when we sit down to meditate. Indeed, one well-known meditation teacher recently pointed out that our modern-day brains have to process as much information in a day as our ancestors just 100 years ago would have had to process in their entire lifetime! But you can make technology work for, instead of against, you with meditation apps and online training. It's also worth considering some of the following accessories to help ease you into a more meditative state of being.

SCENTED CANDLE
Neom Complete Bliss Candle (1 wick), £30 for 185g; neomorganics.com
The sense of smell is very powerful and can build up strong associations with past experiences. Using the same scented candle each time you meditate can help your brain move into a meditative state more easily. These 100 per cent natural candles burn for 35 hours, and are made with pure vegetable wax and up to 24 pure essential oils to naturally enhance your feelings of wellbeing. Chose the therapeutic benefits to suit your needs – Complete Bliss contains Moroccan blush rose, lime and black pepper to soothe mind and body, while Happiness harnesses the power of neroli, mimosa and lemon to help you balance your emotions and leave you feeling more positive.

BUDDHA

Having an image or ornament of an inspiring person or deity such as a Buddha can help to create a quality of stillness and contemplation in your home or meditation area. As we can't all get to India or Thailand to find our ideal Buddha statue, it's worth looking in less auspicious places such as online, in gift shops, antique fairs or even garden centres. As long as the statue pleases you visually and you have a good feeling about the person/place you buy it from, its authenticity is less important. It is a symbol after all, and as you meditate with it, the energy it represents will grow.

Having an image or ornament of a deity such as Buddha can help create stillness or contemplation in your home

JOURNAL

Kikki.K Mindfulness Journal, £21; kikki-K.com

Having a dedicated place to record your mindfulness journey can help you commit to your practice. This beautiful journal from Kikki.K includes inspiring quotes, mini-meditations and mindfulness techniques, interspersed between blank, month-by-month pages where you can set your intentions, record what you've learnt, make notes on what has worked for you and rethink what you may need to revisit or refine. Use it to help you learn how to welcome greater awareness, clarity and acceptance into your life, and celebrate the increased sense of presence that comes from living with mindfulness.

MEDITATION CUSHION

Yogamatters Crescent Cushion, £25; yogamatters.com

While you can sit on the floor to meditate, raising your sitting bones with a meditation cushion helps align your spine, making it more comfortable to sit for longer periods. As it is usual to sit on the edge of a meditation cushion, a crescent shape offers more support to your upper thighs, while the pleats mean it's less likely to split and you can adjust the filling level, making it firmer or softer, to suit.

TIBETAN BELL

Yogamatters Om Tingsha Tibetan Bell, £12.50; yogamatters.com

Using a Tibetan bell to mark the beginning and end of your meditation is a beautiful way to draw your attention inwards. These traditional prayer chimes are hand cast by Tibetan artists and feature an engraving of the Om symbol, which represents the vibrational sound that created the universe. They are available in small, medium and large sizes (from £7.50-£15).

ONLINE MEDITATION

INSIGHT TIMER

Available for iOS and Android, this free app has a whopping 4,000 meditations from acclaimed teachers including Jack Kornfield, Tara Brach, and Sharon Salzberg. You can also follow your own meditations while listening to ambient sounds or intermittent Tibetan bells, plus there are talks and podcasts. You may find it frustrating to see on the screen that 3,000 others have been meditating at the same time, but it's a small price to pay given all the material available to enrich your meditation experience. Get it on iTunes or Google play.

AURA

If you want simplicity, the Aura app offers a personalised three-minute meditation each day, based on answers to questions about your age, stress levels and how interested you are in mindfulness. Also, each time you log in you tell Aura your mood and it suggests appropriate meditations for you. And there are calming sounds to listen to, a guided breathing practice, plus a gratitude feature. It's available free on iTunes or Google play.

MINDFULNESS TRAINING

This seven-week course by George Langenberg at ekhartyoga.com contains guided meditations, including the mindfulness of breathing, the raisin exercise and the body scan. There are also talks, practices such as mindful yoga, 'homework' and a handbook. It's a really supportive way to begin your mindfulness journey. You need to join Ekhart Yoga to take part, but just sign up for a month and try the mindfulness training before deciding if you want to be a member. It's worth the £10.60 a month fee.

MEDITATIONS

Now that you have a deeper understanding of what mindfulness is, you'll be keen to get started. In this chapter, we'll introduce the key exercises and meditations you need to experience for yourself just how supportive mindfulness can be. You'll discover the special nature of a beginner's mind and learn to become more conscious of your breathing. Meanwhile, our body scanning exercise could be the beginning of a lifelong journey of getting to know yourself better. We'll also show you ways to feel more grounded whatever situation you're in, and help you bring more joy and happiness into your life and the lives of those around you, with a loving kindness meditation.

GETTING *started*

Anything is possible as a meditation beginner and, if you hold onto this feeling, you'll reap the benefits

When you begin to meditate for the first time, you enter a world of the unknown; anything is possible. In meditation circles, this is often referred to as the beginner's mind. Everything is new and fresh, as if you've never seen or heard it before, and as a result, anything is possible, and it's a wonderful quality to bring to your mindfulness meditations. In fact, it's an attitude you can bring into your life every day with every breath. It will help you to stay in the moment, and reap the benefits of living your life to the full.

SETTING THE SCENE

A quiet space with no distractions from your mobile or the internet goes without saying. And if you live with others, ask them not to disturb you until your session has finished. There's nothing like a loud knock at the door or your name being called out to bring you abruptly out of the contact you've established in your meditation. It's also a good idea to attend to anything that might distract you. Get an extra blanket or pair of socks now in case you feel cold. If there's something

you need to do later but are worried you may forget about, write it down. It's better if the room isn't overly warm, as that will increase the chance of you drifting off, especially as your meditations increase in length. Set the temperature to a cooler setting or open a window, and cover yourself with a shawl or blanket.

A clean, uncluttered space will help you clear your mind and if you can create a dedicated area to meditate in, even better. Over time, you'll associate the area with feelings of calm, and being centred, which will help you drop into a meditative state more easily. You might also like to have calming, grounding objects around you, such as a small Buddha, a candle or an inspiring image or photograph. A small bell or Tibetan singing bowl is a wonderful addition too. Use it to open and close your meditation. It can also help to create a sense of mindful attention.

An uncluttered space will help you clear your mind and if you can create a dedicated area to meditate in, even better

HOW TO SIT

There is no special posture you need to sit in to practise mindfulness exercises. In many ways, the very act of adopting a specific pose to meditate in can be counterproductive – if you're not careful, you can end up making an unhelpful separation between mindfulness and everyday life. When you tell yourself, 'Now I'm going to sit on my mat and be mindful', after you're finished, you could be in danger of sub-consciously thinking, 'Now I'm getting on with my everyday life – the mindfulness aspect of my day is complete.'

If you're used to sitting crossed-legged on the floor, perhaps as a result of your yoga practice, that's fine, and you might want to do that also when you meditate. If you notice that your back curves, or your knees are higher than your hips, it's a good idea to sit on a yoga block, bolster or even a thick hardback book (you could cover it with a blanket for comfort). This will tilt your pelvis slightly forwards, and enable you to maintain a more naturally aligned spine. You can also sit on a hardbacked chair, with your feet flat on the floor. In fact, many meditation teachers actively encourage this, as it enables you to feel more grounded as you practise.

INTRODUCTION TO
mindful eating

Explore the sensations you get from eating to keep your mind in the present moment

*I*f you've never **formally meditated before, this mindful eating exercise is a really useful place to start**. Many of us are daunted by the prospect of emptying our minds, but this exercise is designed to offer you plenty of opportunities to focus your mind on the present moment. Used as an introduction to meditation in his mindfulness-based stress reduction programme, Jon Kabat-Zinn suggests using a raisin to explore the sensations of eating, but you can choose any small piece of food you like – however, the texture and intensity of taste in a raisin makes it an ideal choice. The exercise will only take about five minutes, but you still need to do it at a time when you won't be disturbed. Turn off your phone, place the raisin on a plate in front of you and give your full awareness to each section of the exercise.

THE TECHNIQUE

Take a few moments to centre yourself. Gently close your eyes and bring your attention to your breath. Without actively trying to change anything, allow your breath to settle naturally and deepen.

When you're ready to begin, open your eyes and look at the raisin as if you've never seen one before. After a few moments, place it in the palm of your hand or hold it in between your finger and thumb. Keep looking. Be curious. Notice the way the skin folds in on itself, the varying textures and shades, the wiggly patterns. Observe how the light falls on it, creating highlights on the creases and shadows in the crevices. Give the raisin your complete attention, turning it round to see the back, the sides, the top.

If you find yourself thinking, 'What on earth am I doing?' or 'This is a waste of time', acknowledge the words as thoughts, perhaps saying the word 'thinking', and then return to your observations.

Carefully, bring the raisin to your nose and, as you breathe in, become aware of anything you notice. Does the raisin have an odour? Then bring it to your ear and move it around between your fingers. Do you notice any sound? Does the sound change if you alter the pressure between your fingers?

The raisin exercise is the perfect introduction to mindful eating

Explore different tastes and textures by choosing a different food each time you do the exercise

Slowly bring the raisin to your mouth. You could try this with your eyes closed and, if so, notice how your hand knows exactly where to go to take the raisin to your lips. Is there any reaction in your mouth as you bring the raisin towards it? Next, gently place the raisin on your tongue and close your mouth. Without doing anything, not yet chewing, become aware of the sensations happening in your mouth. Again, without chewing, move the raisin around your mouth with your tongue. What do you notice? When you're ready, consciously bite into the raisin. What sensations do you feel? Slowly chew the raisin, noticing how it changes in your mouth, and any accompanying thoughts you have.

When you're ready to swallow the raisin, pause for a moment, and consciously slow down the impulse. Can you sense where the swallowing movement wants to begin? Can you trace the pattern of muscle activity as you swallow? Do you feel the raisin travelling down your throat? See if you can notice any sensation in your mouth once it is empty once more, or if you feel any difference in your stomach or lower belly? Can you sense any difference in being one raisin heavier? Continue to sit for a few moments to allow your body to absorb the effects of the exercise. Then, when you're ready, gently return to your day, allowing some of the mindful stillness you have encountered to stay with you.

HOW TO WORK WITH THIS EXERCISE

This is a great introduction to mindful eating, and you might like to repeat this exercise a few times, perhaps using a raisin each time, so you can observe how your sensitivity develops with experience. You could also explore different tastes and textures by choosing a different food each time you do the exercise.

To take mindful eating into your everyday life, you might like to make a commitment to take one mindful bite each day or at every meal. As you feel ready, and time permits, you could increase this to include one snack a day or one meal a day. Gradually, over time, you'll learn to become more mindful in your eating and won't need to eat so slowly to appreciate the multitude of sensations you experience while eating.

After time, you can use the sensitivity you develop to decide what to eat. Before you chose what to buy for your lunch or prepare for supper, tune in to your mouth and body, and ask it what it really needs to eat.

Allow yourself to become fully immersed in the body scan and notice any physical sensations you experience

THE
body scan
EXERCISE

Focus on individual parts of your
body to bring your attention to
the here and now

**ow that you
have some
experience
of how it feels
to focus your
attention on
a single object, such as a raisin, you
can begin to expand your sensitivity
to rest your awareness on your body.**
In the body scan practice, you
systematically direct your attention to
different parts of your anatomy –
sometimes to a small, precise point, for
example your little toe and, at others, to
a larger, generalised area, perhaps one
that includes your pelvis and the whole
of your legs. You could think of the body
scan as a way to start training your mind
to adjust its focus at will, all the while
staying in the present moment. One thing
that's important to remember is that,
although you may feel more relaxed
afterwards, this is not a relaxation

exercise. The purpose of the body scan
is to simply notice what you're
experiencing in the current moment.

FEEL YOUR BODY
Allow yourself to become fully immersed
in the exercise and notice any physical
sensations you experience, such as heat
or cold, tightness or relaxation, tingling,
pulsing or numbness, and be aware of
the difference between the sensations
on your skin surface and those deep
within your body. You may find you
experience quite intense feelings in
some places, while other sensations may
be so subtle you can hardly feel them.

You may also become aware of
emotional responses associated with
different parts of your body, or perhaps
a memory will appear or you'll notice
that a particular thought is connected
to a specific body part. This is quite
normal. Our relationship with our body is

often a complex one, fuelled in part by
cultural expectations, the media and
past experiences. In this practice, rather
than losing yourself in any thoughts or
emotions you experience, or perhaps
trying to reject or change them, simply
have the intention to stay as present
as you can in the current felt moment,
letting thoughts, feelings and even the
physical sensations themselves, arise
and fade like images on a screen.

And, finally, don't worry about whether
or not you are 'doing it right' – there is
nothing to get right or wrong – you are
just bringing your conscious attention
to what *is*, right here, right now. As with
the raisin exercise, if your mind starts
to wander – and it probably will – gently
bring it back to your breath, and the
sensations you're feeling in your body.
And if you fall asleep – again, which
you may – simply continue the sequence
when you wake up.

THE TECHNIQUE

Chose a time and place where you won't be interrupted – you'll need about 30 minutes – and lie on your back on a soft surface with your arms by your sides, palms facing upwards, and your feet falling out to the sides. If this isn't possible, simply lie in a way that is comfortable for you. What is most important is that you come to the practice with an open, enquiring mind. Jon Kabat-Zinn describes the body scan as an 'opportunity to fall awake', alert to this present moment, so stay as close to your experience as you can, and with kind, non-judgemental attention.

1 Gently close your eyes and, for a few moments, simply allow your body and mind to become quiet. Let your thoughts begin to settle and your heart slow down. When you feel ready, bring your attention to your breath and, without trying to change anything, simply notice how your body is responding right now. Perhaps your lower belly is rising on the in-breath and gently falling on the out-breath, or maybe you feel your chest expanding and contracting. You may be aware of the back of your ribs compressing against the floor or mat as you inhale, or perhaps you feel a cool sensation in your nostrils as the air passes through them on the way to your lungs. There's nothing to change, just observe what is happening to your body as a whole as you breathe, moment by moment. Notice if thoughts start to overtake experience, and gently bring your attention back to your body.

2 When the moment feels right, softly transfer your attention to the toes of your left foot, perhaps identifying your big toe, and then your little toe. Notice if you can distinguish the three middle toes as well. What sensations do you feel here? Can you feel your toes touching? Are they warm? Do you feel any moisture? Are the sensations pleasant to you or unpleasant? Perhaps you don't feel anything at all. Simply give your undivided attention to your toes and notice what is there. Maybe some thoughts will arise – perhaps you don't like the look of your feet, or maybe they remind you you're due for a pedicure! You might start to feel bored, impatient or sad. Gently let go of any thoughts or feelings and let yourself sink back into the sensations of the present moment.

Use your breath as a guide and point of focus, by imagining your in-breath travelling from your nose to your torso and down your left leg to the tips of your toes, and your out-breath travelling back up your legs to your lungs and out through your nostrils. After a few moments, take a deep inhale, then as you exhale, let go of the connection to your toes, and allow your attention to rest on the sole of your left foot. Become acutely aware of any and every sensation you feel here, then gradually turn your

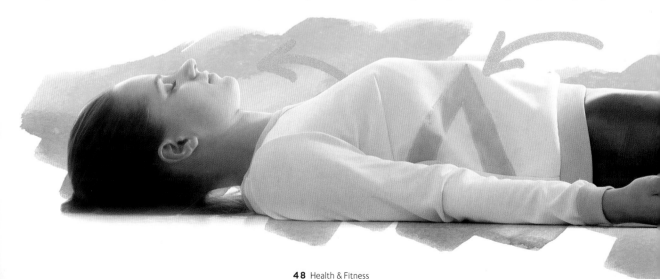

attention to the top of your foot, then your ankle. As with your toes, take your breath right down to your foot on the inhale and back up on the exhale.

3 After a deep inhale, exhale as you let go of your focus on your foot and shift your attention onto your left calf, sensing not just the muscles and skin surface, but deep into your bones. Continue moving in this way to incorporate more and more of your body, travelling next to your left knee, thigh and hip, all the time allowing yourself to rest in the present moment, content to just be with whatever is. After pausing for a moment at your left hip, take your attention to your right toes, and repeat the process with your right leg.

4 Coming from your right hip, let your attention nestle into your pelvis. Feeling the sensation of weight as your sacrum rests on the mat, breathe fully into your pelvis, allowing your awareness to expand into the area as you deeply

inhale, softening and releasing on the exhale. Then spend a few moments experiencing both your legs and your pelvis at the same time. Feel the expanse of your thighs, the areas of pressure where your body is touching the mat, your heels sinking into the floor. After a few moments, bring your attention to your lower back, feeling exactly what is here, right now. Breathe into the area and let yourself experience what it feels like to simply be, before letting go on an exhale and moving onto your abdomen.

5 Using this pattern of breathing in and out from the body area you're focusing on, move next to your chest, and then the fingertips of your left hand, travelling up to your left shoulder. Repeat the pattern with the fingertips of your right hand to your right shoulder, then feel your chest and arms as a whole. Keep breathing into your body and feeling what is here for you right now.

6 Gently take your attention to your neck and throat, then your face, tuning in to the minute sensations of your lips and mouth, eyes and eyelids. Soften your forehead and your temples, becoming aware of your ears. Breathe in to each area, experiencing what is present for you.

7 Next, give your attention to your body as an entity, breathing in to your whole body. Feel it open and expand, soften and release. Experience your body just as it is. Feel present and fully awake in this moment.

8 When you feel ready to come out of the body scan, very gently take a few deep breaths and become aware of the ground beneath you. Gently wriggle your fingers and toes, and stretch your body in a way that feels right for you, before slowly opening your eyes and coming back to sitting. You may find it helpful to make a note of some of your experiences in a journal, so you can see how they develop and change over repeated practice.

TAKE IT *further*

Deepen the benefits with
this second, more advanced
body scan exercise

hile you can work very deeply with the
body scan technique – monks and nuns
at the UK's Amravati Buddhist Monastery
will spend an entire day doing the
practice – another way to develop the
exercise is to take a more anatomical approach. You can do the
following practice either lying on the floor or sitting on a straight-
backed chair. If you haven't done anything like this before, simply be
open to your experience – it can sometimes take time to develop this
kind of sensitivity. Spend around 30 minutes with this practice.

**ORDER OF
TRAVEL**

1. Muscles
2. Skin
3. Muscles
4. Organs
5. Skeleton
6. Outside body
7. Skin

3

After about five minutes, let go of the connection to your skin and take your attention to your muscles. Can you feel the expanse of your calves? The bulk of your quads? Focus first on large muscle groups or areas of tension, as they will be easiest to locate, then notice if you sense any of the smaller muscles. Can you feel the muscles around your eyes or your lips, for example?

4

Now move to your organs. This practice needs a little more sensitivity. Perhaps starting with your heart, take your attention to the centre of your chest. Do you feel anything here? Can you sense the space that your heart is occupying? After a few moments, travel with awareness to your right side torso. Attune your sensitivity to the large area where your liver is situated. It's fine if you don't sense anything, simply allow your attention to rest in the relevant areas.

2

When you feel ready to begin, bring your awareness to your skin surface, seeing if you can sense the skin on the whole of your body, from your toes to the crown of your head. Where can you feel your skin? Are there any areas that you cannot sense? Is there heat? Coolness? Can you feel a draught on your skin?

1

Gently close your eyes and begin by centring yourself. Take a few deep breaths into your belly, inhaling through your nose and exhaling through an open mouth on an audible sigh, 'ahhh'. As you breathe out, feel your muscles releasing and your weight sinking downwards. Then allow your breath to return to its natural rhythm and rest for a couple of minutes as your heart rate begins to settle.

5

Next, take your attention to your skeleton. Can you feel the bones in your legs? Your fingers? With gentle focus and concentration, allow your awareness to rest on your bones and notice anything that comes forwards such as a sense of their contours, density or any painful areas.

7

Finally, return once more to your skin surface, allow the feeling to register, then release it. Spend a few moments quietly with yourself then gently open your eyes.

6

When you feel ready, return to your skin surface, reconnect with it, then allow your awareness to expand into the area surrounding your body. You might like to stay close to your skin surface, or explore areas further away from your body. Don't worry if it feels strange to you – the simplest way to describe the process is like tuning a radio, you're moving around in an area to see what is present. For now, simply notice how it feels to sense the space around you.

5

ways to feel more
PRESENT

Have you noticed how some people look as if a gust of wind could knock them off balance, while others seem as solid as a rock, even if they're slim? It's not just a question of weight or body shape either, people who appear to have a sense of stability and confidence in their body are likely to be grounded. A term often used in psychotherapy and yoga circles, being grounded refers to being fully present in the current moment, and feeling energetically connected to your lower body and the earth beneath you. If you have a lot of energy in your head, for example, your thoughts are likely to be racing, your jaw may be clenched or you may have a throbbing headache. Excessive energy in your torso may show as butterflies in the stomach or a pounding heart.

When you're grounded, your energy is more weighted in the lower body – in your pelvis, legs and feet. The corresponding feelings are of solidity and balance, and an inner confidence that the earth beneath you is strong enough to support you. Whether from fear, anxiety, low self-esteem or habit, it's surprising how many people tense the muscles of their legs, pelvis and stomach as if to hold their weight off the ground, rather than relax into it. Use the following exercises whenever you want to experience the present moment more fully, and to build an increasing connection to the ground beneath you.

1 GET DOWN TO IT

One way to consciously bring your energy downwards is to sequentially focus on releasing any tension in your body from your head downwards.

GIVE IT A TRY: Take your attention to particular areas of your body, notice if any tension is held there and consciously release the muscle on an out breath. Key areas to consider include your temples, jaw, lips and the back of your neck. As you travel down your body, identify and let go of any tension in your shoulders, arms, belly and buttocks. If you're sitting, you can spend some time imagining you're releasing the weight of your body through your sitting bones. Continue taking your attention down your legs, sensing if there is any tension and releasing it as you exhale. When you get to your feet, spend a few moments becoming aware of any sensations there, then rest your attention on the soles of your feet. If it feels comfortable, imagine your legs extending into the ground like roots.

WHEN TO USE IT: This exercise is ideal to use any time your mind is overactive or you are feeling stressed. It's a great way to practise when you a have a few otherwise wasted minutes, such as standing in a queue at a checkout or waiting for an appointment. You could even practise it before you eat a meal – by quietening your thoughts you'll be able to eat in a mindful way.

2 Hands-on healing

Scientific research shows that moving different parts of your hands activates different areas of your brain. In yoga philosophy, mudras (hand gestures) help generate feelings of calm, focus and wellbeing by aiding the flow of energy (prana) around your body. Most of the major energy channels start or finish in your hands or feet, so working with your hands is an effective way to clear blockages in these channels and bring you into a place of balance, says Swami Saradananda, author of Mudras for Modern Life (Watkins, £12.99).

GIVE IT A TRY: Known as the wisdom gesture (or jnana mudra), this hand position helps you feel more grounded. Sit in a comfortable crossed-leg position and join the tip of each index finger with the thumb of the same hand to form a circle. Apply a slight pressure. Let your free fingers be slightly extended but still relaxed. Gently rest the insides of your wrists on your knees with your palms facing inwards and your fingertips pointing down. Softly close your eyes and breathe into your belly, remaining in the pose as long as feels comfortable.

WHEN TO USE IT: You can practise this mudra at home each day to build up a background reserve of feeling grounded, or in situations where you want to come back to your centre, such as on your commute home from work.

3 GO ON A SENSORY JOURNEY

Tuning in to your body is vital if you're to feel more grounded. This exercise works by giving your mind something to concentrate on, while counting down to a single point focuses you in the now. Don't rush the exercise or you won't get the benefits. Afterwards, breathe into your belly for a moment before getting on with your day.

GIVE IT A TRY: The technique is simple, just find:

5 things you can see
4 things you can touch
3 things you can hear
2 things you can smell
1 thing you can taste

Do the following for a deeper experience.

✦ **SIGHT:** It may be tempting to tick off the first five things you lay your eyes on, so slow it down by resting your attention for a few moments on each of the five objects you chose. Rather than tensing the muscles around your eyes and zooming in on the object, soften your gaze and see if you can allow the object to 'come to you', by allowing yourself to receive its qualities through your eyes. Pause for a while, letting your eyes rest on the object, then move on to the next one.

✦ **TOUCH:** Again, rather than rattling off a list of things you can feel, quietly become aware of the areas where your body is touching another surface – the seat of a chair or the floor. Mentally, spend time at each area, noticing your bodily sensations. For example, at first you may just feel your sitting bones on the chair, but as you sink into the experience you may sense the area of contact expanding, so you begin to feel the compression in your buttocks. Take your time – and breathe!

✦ **HEARING:** As you tune in to your sense of hearing, focus on three distinct sounds. Are they constant or do they change? Is there a regular pattern? If the sound changes, see if you can trace it from its begining to its end. For example, a car getting louder as it approaches then fading into the distance. The softer the sound, the quieter you need to be to hear it. Become aware of the space between the sounds, notice the stillness and absorb its effects.

✦ **SMELL:** You can approach this in two ways. First, you can breathe in and notice if there's anything you can smell around you. This may take a little practise and it helps if you close your eyes. If you don't sense anything straight away, go to different areas in your home, or if out, keep walking until you catch a scent of something. Pause, and absorb its fragrance, imagining you're breathing it in to every cell of your body. The second way is to choose an item, the sleeve of your cardigan, say, bring it to your nose and sniff! This sense is strongly associated with memory, so if anything you smell reminds you of the past, gently bring yourself back to the present, maybe chosing a different item to explore, and continue with the exercise.

✦ **TASTE:** If you're at home or work, it's probably easy to find something to taste, or you could carry a raisin or two with you (p44)! If you're out, you could explore your mouth. Run your tongue over the outer and inner surfaces of your teeth, draw your inner cheeks togther to see if you have a 'taste' in your mouth.

WHEN TO USE IT: This technique is often used to help people who have panic attacks stay anchored in the present. But it's also a wonderful way to tune into your senses and reconnect to your body when you're feeling stuck in your head.

4 Rock on

Energy follows attention, so bringing your awareness to your legs and feet will help bring any excess energy from your upper body into your lower body, helping you to feel more centred and grounded. Do the following execise in loose clothing and in socks or bare feet. If you can do it outside on grass, even better.

GIVE IT A TRY: Stand with your feet hip-width apart and centre yourself by focusing on your breath. Step forwards with your right foot, then slowly transfer your weight from your back foot to your front foot, allowing your back heel to come off the floor. Inhale. Pause your breath as you transfer your weight back into your left foot, allowing your front toes to come off the ground. Exhale. Finding a rhythm, rock backwards and forwards for three to five minutes and repeat on the other side. Once you're familiar with it, you can focus on the base of your spine while you rock. This can help bring a greater sense of grounding.

WHEN TO USE IT: Regular practice of this over a period of weeks will help you build up a permanent feeling of being grounded. You can also use it before an event you're feel anxious about.

5 BODY DROPS

This is a really powerful technique from the kundalini yoga tradition, taught by Marlene Smits (ekhartyoga.com), and it's a super-quick way to bring you back into the present. It works on activating your root chakra (situated at the base of your spine), the energy centre associated with the feeling of grounding, stability and security in the world.

GIVE IT A TRY: Sit in a comfortable crossed-leg position on a carpet or yoga mat. If you are able, you can place one one foot on the opposite thigh in a half lotus position. Make your hands into fists and place them, palms inwards, on the mat next to your hips. Push yourself up from your fists, then drop yourself back down, gradually building up speed, and bounce up and down up to 30 seconds. The move may release some tension in the form of emotion, so don't be surprised if you start laughing! After 30 seconds, inhale, exhale and then be still for a while to allow your body to absorb the experience.

WHEN TO USE IT: Avoid this exercise if you have any back problems such as a herniated disc. Otherwise, use it whever you feel spaced out, over active or insecure.

SIMPLE
meditations

Use these easy practices
throughout the day to quieten
your mind and centre yourself

If there was a pill that could boost your memory, focus and cognitive skills, while reducing stress and anxiety at the same time, most people would be tempted to give it a try. And what if it enhanced happiness, self-esteem, and energy levels too, while improving your immunity and lessening your risk of arthritis – all with no side effects?

Meditation has many scientifically proven benefits, but perhaps the over-riding sense of calm it brings is the one that attracts most people. Here are three practices to get you started.

1 CONSCIOUS BREATHING

There are many breathing practices you can use to help you quieten your mind and come back into the present moment. One of the simplest comes from zen monk and founder of Plum Village in France, Thich Naht Hahn. You can practise this breathing exercise in any way that works for you, taking time out of your schedule to sit for five or 10 minutes on your yoga mat, or using it throughout the day when you want return to a quieter space inside yourself.

Try it on your daily commute, while waiting for a kettle to boil or to have a pause between activities so you can recalibrate and continue with your day in a more centred way.

Sitting, lying or standing in a comfortable position, as you breathe in, silently repeat the words 'Breathing in, I know that I am breathing in.' And as you breathe out, say 'Breathing out, I know that I am breathing out.' Be as relaxed as you are able, allowing your body to gently expand as you inhale, and to soften and release as you exhale. Don't rush yourself, but let the practice naturally deepen your breathing. Gradually, your mind will settle and your heartbeat will become slower. Once you're used to the practice, you can even abbreviate the words, so you just say 'in' as you breathe in, and 'out' as you breathe out. This meditation is a useful way to link your mind with your body.

Another simple breathing practice from Thich Naht Hahn is to recite the following lines silently to yourself as you mindfully breathe in and out. 'Breathing in, I calm my body; Breathing out, I smile; Dwelling in the present moment, I know this is a wonderful moment.' As he says, 'Our appointment with life is in the present moment.'

> *'Breathing in, I calm my body; Breathing out, I smile; Dwelling in the present moment, I know this is a wonderful moment.'*

2 COUNTING THE BREATH

You may be familiar with a different technique for helping you connect to your breath and calm your mind's natural tendency to flit from one thing to another. Counting your breath is a time honoured way to help you stay focused in the present moment. Again, you can dedicate a specific time for this practice, or integrate it into your everyday activities.

Sitting, standing or lying down, take a natural breath in, followed by a breath out. After the out-breath, count 'one'. Then breathe in again and out again, and count 'two'. Continue breathing and counting in this pattern until you reach '10', and then return to the beginning and start with 'one' again. Some people suggest stopping every time you notice your mind has started to wander, and returning to the beginning, counting from 'one'. If you do this, you may notice you never get much beyond 'two' or 'three', as the mind loves nothing more than to flit from one subject to another! It's a bit like a puppy that needs to be gently trained. Perhaps experiment with both methods to see which one works best for you. For other ways to work with counting the breath, take a look at the Buddhist meditation practices on p60.

3 GAZING AT AN OBJECT

You may have come across a simple meditation practice where you focus your attention on a single object, such as the flame of a candle. Those of you who have tried it might have found that as soon as you begin, your mind is flooded with thoughts, ranging from how uncomfortable it is to sit crossed-legged on the floor, to what you're having for supper that evening.

A yoga meditation technique from the 2nd century Indian sage Patanjali, wisely

'IT WORKED FOR ME'

Rebecca Johnson, 36.
'I chose an ink pen to do this meditation, and when I began, forced myself to think of as many things as I could about the pen, simply to crowd out the other thoughts in my mind. The technique worked, but it went further than that. I soon began to appreciate the essence of a simple pen. The outer shell that protected the ink within. The ink – the lifeblood – with its potential to communicate life or death messages, to share a person's history, their passions and fears. The pen as a keeper of secrets, stories and truth. The nib – a point of concentration. How everything had to come into focus, be channeled through the narrowest of points to find expression in the world. It's a bit like the way we need to refine and distil our thoughts if we are to express them wisely in words. I came to understand how being mindful can bring a sense of humility to oneself and a deep appreciation of how even the simplest of objects are so much richer when fully experienced in the present moment. I understood how precious our lives would become if we brought this quality of attention even to a fraction of our experience.'

takes the nature of the busy mind into account. In his *Yoga Sutras*, he divides meditation into two processes: 'samprajnata' with thoughts, and 'asamprajnata' (without thoughts). Working with thoughts is a very useful place to start when you're new to meditation.

In this meditation, Patanjali lets you make a deal with your mind. So you say to yourself, 'OK, you can think about anything you want to as long as it relates to this candle'. Rather than rigidly tell yourself, you must have no thoughts at all, you mindfully and gradually restrict the range of things your mind thinks about.

You can choose any object you like for this practice, it doesn't have to be a candle. Simply set aside 10 to 15 minutes when you won't be disturbed, and place your chosen object a few feet away from you, ideally at eye level. This is so you don't tire your neck by looking down at too acute an angle. Find a comfortable sitting position – on a chair with a straight back is fine, if you don't like the floor – close your eyes and spend a few moments connecting to your breath. Let it soften and slow a little, until it finds its natural rhythm. When you feel ready, gently open your eyes and gaze at the object, focusing on it alone, and giving yourself permission to have any thoughts you wish – but about the object only. When you're ready to finish, gently close your eyes, breathe into your belly and allow yourself to absorb your experiences. You may find it useful to repeat the exercise a few times, and make notes in your mindfulness journal about your observations. You'll learn much!

LOVING
kindness

Feelings of love, joy and pain relief
are just a few of the benefits of
practising this meditation

*T*he loving-kindness
meditation, also
known as metta,
is a Buddhist
practice that dates
back more than 2,500 years. Its full
name, metta bhavana comes from the Pali
language – metta means non-romantic
love, friendliness or kindness, and
bhavana – to cultivate – and recent
research has found this ancient practice
to have a wealth of benefits.

A study in the *Journal of Personality and
Social Psychology* revealed that seven
weeks of practising metta increased
feelings of love, joy, contentment,
gratitude and amusement, leading to
a greater sense of purpose in life and
fewer symptoms of illness. But the
benefits go beyond making you feel
positive. Studies have shown it can bring
immediate relief for migraine sufferers
(a 33 per cent reduction in pain and a
43 per cent decrease in emotional
tension after just one 20-minute session);
significantly ease chronic lower back
pain; improve post-traumatic stress relief;
increase your respiratory sinus arrhythmia
(an indication of your ability to enter a
restorative state) and slow your breathing
rate – meaning you relax more.

Evidence also shows it makes you less
self-critical; more compassionate and
helpful; it increases empathy and makes
you feel more part of society. Research
shows it's even anti-ageing – women who
practise the loving-kindness meditation,
have longer telomere lengths than a
control group (shorter telomeres are linked
to accelerated ageing). What's not to love!

May I be filled with
loving kindness.
May I be well.
May I be peaceful
and at ease.
May I be happy

'May you be well, healthy and strong.
May you be happy.
May you abide in peace.
May you feel safe and secure.
May you feel loved and cared for'

HOW TO DO IT

Begin, as usual by centring yourself and letting your breath slow down. Then, acknowledge any thoughts that come into your mind and let them pass by like clouds in an empty sky. When you feel quieter, move on to the practice as directed below. You can use any of the phrases dotted around these pages, but feel free to change or adjust them so that they resonate with your own experience.

STAGE ONE Begin to silently repeat the words you have chosen, focusing on yourself. For example, 'May I be filled with loving kindness…' Let your breath find a natural rhythm. You may want to repeat one phrase on the in-breath, the next on the out-breath, or you might prefer to breathe in and out, and then say a phrase. Experiment and find what works best for you, using your breath to allow the feeling of relaxation and calm to expand within you. You can also use images to encourage the development of loving kindness. The

Buddha suggests picturing yourself as a young and much-loved child, or you might like to imagine yourself being bathed in soft golden light that surrounds and fills your body. You could also choose a memory of when you felt unconditional love and then, letting go of the memory, stay with the feeling of love.

STAGE TWO When you feel ready, either after the above practice or on a separate occasion, bring to mind someone you love deeply – a friend, partner or parent, perhaps. Allow your thoughts to dwell on this person and connect to your feelings for them, then repeat the phrase you've been using, this time changing the words to 'May *he/she* be filled with loving kindness…'. Some practitioners also suggest having your awareness on your heart area, sensing it becoming more open and visualising soft light gently travelling from your heart to theirs.

STAGE THREE The next stage of this practice is to choose someone you feel neutral about. Perhaps a friend of a friend that you rarely see, or a colleague who sits on the other side of the office to you. As you repeat the phrases, simply hold them in your awareness, and offer these kindly feelings for their wellbeing.

STAGE FOUR Next, move on to someone you don't like or have difficult feelings towards. This may seem as if it's going to be very difficult, but once you've established a bedrock of compassion towards yourself, it's easier to feel compassion for others. Rather

than becoming absorbed in any emotions *you* may be feeling towards this person, see if you can simply allow yourself to focus on them and their need for more loving kindness in their life.

STAGE FIVE The final stage of the practice is to offer loving kindness to all beings – those you know and those you don't know. As you become more experienced, if you wish, you can include the five stages in your 20-minute meditation.

TO FINISH, gradually let your mind become still again and spend a few moments absorbing the effects of your experience. Over time, the practice will bring you many things, including a greater sense of calm and connection to the world.

Jack Kornfield meditation teacher and author of *No Time Like the Present* (Rider, £12.99) suggests repeating the loving-kindness meditation over and over for 15-20 minutes once or twice a day for several months. If this seems a big commitment, remember you can easily fit it into your normal day's activities, for example by using your commute to work, saying it in bed before you go to sleep or while you cook your supper. As a beginner, aim to start with five minutes, and don't worry if it feels unnatural or awkward at first or makes you feel irritated. Just accept these feelings, and be patient and kind with yourself. The feelings will soon change.

'May she be happy,
May she be healthy,
May she be free from all pain'

MOVING MEDITATIONS

Once you have some experience of the foundations of mindfulness – bringing your attention to your breath, and observing your thoughts, emotions and bodily sensations in a non-judgemental way – the next stage is to put your understanding into practice. Moving meditations are perfect for this as, rather than learning to be mindful while dealing with the multiple demands of everyday life, you choose one area at a time to practise your new-found skills. We've included four moving meditations where you can apply the insights you've learnt so far. Whether you prefer to walk, run, swim or practise yoga, the following pages will give you all you need to get started.

Peace
IS EVERY
STEP

Walking meditations not only
allow you to become more aware,
they also ease stressful feelings

e're usually so preoccupied with getting to our destination that we often miss out on the beauty of the journey and the company of the one friend we will always have – ourselves. The wind rustling in the trees, the shape of a cloud, a spontaneous smile from a passer-by… all these moments are lost as we rush from place to place, rarely attending to where we are right now. Jon Kabat-Zinn, founder of mindfulness-based stress reduction, frequently reminds us that this moment is all we have. The past has truly gone, and if we always look to the future, we will never find peace or happiness in the present. Walking meditations are a wonderful opportunity to go on a journey with, and into, yourself, using the rhythm of your footsteps and breath to become more fully embodied with awareness. Use them as a standalone practice to develop your sensitivity and presence, and when you're feeling stressed.

GETTING STARTED

When you first start to practise, you might like to find a secluded area, maybe in your garden so you don't feel self-conscious, or even in your home. Set aside 15-20 minutes and, as with the other meditations in this book, take a moment to centre yourself before you begin, breathing into your lower belly and allowing your mind to quieten. Then, resting your gaze on the ground a few feet in front of you, walk at a slow and steady pace. Once you've begun to build up some experiential understanding of what it means to walk mindfully, you might like to experiment with different paces – walking in extreme slow motion and immersing yourself in every minute sensation in your body, perhaps, or speeding up your pace and noticing if you can rest in mindfulness as you walk a little faster. If your mind starts to wander – and it will! – gently bring your attention back to your footsteps and your breath.

FIND YOUR FEET

This Buddhist walking meditation from the Theravadā tradition is a beautiful way to come into a deeper contact with your body. It's wonderfully calming and grounding, and is a really useful introduction to using movement to teach you to attune to the present moment.

● Find a clear stretch of ground where you can walk in a straight line for 10 to 20 paces. Walking barefoot will give you the most immediate sense of connection with the ground, but if that's not possible, a pair of light shoes with a flexible sole or 'barefoot' shoes will also work.

● Begin by standing with your feet a comfortable distance apart and become aware of the earth beneath you. Feel your legs becoming heavy and solid as you allow any excess tension in your body to sink downwards. Some people like to walk with their hands clasped behind their back as it helps to 'anchor' the hands, creating less distraction than letting the arms swing back and forth with each step. Experiment and find out what works best or you, noticing the different effects of different positions.

● When you're ready to start walking, gently shift your weight onto one leg and begin to raise the heel of your opposite foot. Slowly peel it away from the ground, from heel to toe, until you are momentarily balancing on one leg.

● Take a comfortable step forwards, feeling your heel touch the ground first, then consciously releasing the rest of your foot onto the earth, first the mid-foot, then the ball and finally the toes. Notice how, as you travel forwards, your front leg 'fills up' with weight as you back leg 'empties' and you peel your heel away from the floor once more.

Be aware of all the sensations you are experiencing, the transfer of weight from one leg to the other, the movement of your hips swaying from side to side, the tensing and releasing of the muscles in your legs and buttocks. Simply observe these feelings as they arise and subside. And remember to breathe! It's easy to give so much attention to the process of slow walking or the sensations you're feeling that you hold your breath.

● When you come to the end of your 10-20 paces, bring your back foot forwards to meet your front foot and pause for a moment, experiencing the sense of stillness now surrounding you. Then, very gradually, turn around, re-centre yourself and walk back in the other direction.

Walking barefoot will give you the most immediate sense of connection with the ground

STAY PRESENT

While you're walking, it's likely that many thoughts and, possibly, emotions will come forward. Be kind to yourself as you turn your attention back to walking and your breath. Naming what your mind is doing can be a helpful tool, so each time you notice you have become distracted, say to yourself 'planning', 'thinking' or 'day dreaming', etc. You can also 'label' what you are doing, as a way of staying focused. So, for example, you could say, 'stepping,' for each step that you take, or 'left' and 'right' to correspond with the foot that you're using.

These two techniques are best used when you walk very slowly, otherwise they could become like a marching song! If you prefer to walk at a normal or near-normal pace, you could try counting your steps. In this practice, you take a step and say, 'one'. On your next two steps, you repeat the words 'one, two,' and then, on the next three steps, you say, 'one, two, three,' and so on. Repeat this pattern all the way to 10, and then start again from one. You could also inwardly repeat the loving kindness meditation (p60) as you walk. The most important thing with all walking meditations is that you bring a sensitive, respectful attitude to your practice. As Vietnamese monk Thich Nhat Hahn says: 'Walk as if you are kissing the earth with your feet.'

✳ MINDFUL WALKING ON THE GO

Thich Nhat Hahn suggests using this beautiful gatha, or short verse, to help you stay close to yourself as you walk. This is a practice you can use as you walk about in everyday life. Take two or three steps for each in-breath and the same for each out-breath.

*Breathing in 'I have arrived'
– breathing out 'I am home.'
Breathing in 'In the here'
breathing out 'In the now'.
Breathing in 'I am solid' –
breathing out 'I am free'.
Breathing in 'In the ultimate'
breathing out 'I dwell'.*

Run
FOR IT

Use these techniques to train
more consciously and improve
your running

Mindful running can help you transform negative thoughts, manage pain and even help you recover faster, all by bringing simple, non-judgemental awareness to your thoughts, emotions and physical sensations. It helps you achieve that elusive 'flow state' – where feeling relaxed yet still being highly conscious of your body can make running seem effortless – and enables you to refine your responses to the physical and mental challenges of running. When you next go out on a run, try incorporating these techniques into your session and notice the difference it makes.

1. RUNNING ON AIR

Your breath powers your run, bringing fresh oxygen to your working muscles. Quite simply, the harder you run the harder you'll need to breathe; the slower, the more easeful it will be on your heart and lungs. This interplay of exertion and effort makes it interesting to work mindfully with your breath while running. Experiment with synching your stride with your breath, taking two or three strides to an in-breath and the same for an out-breath, perhaps counting 'in-two-three', 'out-two-three,' and always breathing through your nose. Continue running this way for several minutes, feeling the mesmerising effect of the pattern, then lengthen your breath to take four steps to one inhale, four to an exhale. As your breath adjusts to this new rhythm, slightly extend the pause period between the in and out breaths, perhaps taking a stride or two with no breath. After a while, see if you can maintain the rhythm but let go of counting, feeling the soft quality of awareness you've created by gently working with your breath. Experience the lightness this creates in your stride, as if you really are running on air.

2 Feel the chi

Try following the principles of Chi Running. Based on the ancient art of t'ai chi, Chi Running encourages you to run in harmony with your body's natural energy centres, especially one known as the 'dan tien', situated about five centimetres below your navel. The basic principles of Chi Running include good posture; enlisting the support of gravity by leaning slightly forwards; landing with a mid-foot strike; engaging your core and relaxing your limbs so your legs *support* your body instead of pushing or pulling it forwards; and initiating movement from your centre, or dan tien. Rather than attempt to learn all these techniques at the same time, experiment with one at a time, bringing a beginner's curiosity to the experience and noting what you feel.

3. DON'T FIGHT DISCOMFORT

Pain is no stranger to runners. Whether it's cramping calves, a tight chest or burning quads, instead of following your habitual patterns – tensing your muscles to reduce painful sensations, perhaps, calling it a day or drowning in thoughts of how hard you find it to run – bring mindful attention to the area that is causing you discomfort. There are several ways you can do this. Be curious about the sensations you're feeling. Name them, notice if they have a beginning, a peak in intensity or if they begin to fade, maybe to be replaced with a different sensation elsewhere. You can also direct your in-breath to the area and focus on releasing any sensations of tightness as you exhale. Maybe it's a psychological resistance that's causing you discomfort, such as feeling fatigued, worrying how much further you have to run or even irritation due to boredom. Simply return your attention to your present moment, to the physical experience, and the repetitive sound of your feet on the ground.

4. SURPRISE YOURSELF

Incorporate a beginner's attitude to your run by repeatedly changing your mind as to how you'll run today. If your usual route takes you on one side of the road, cross over and run on the other side. If you normally run in the morning before work, try an evening run just before sunset. Observe the change in the quality of light, what different sounds you notice and how it feels to listen with your whole body. Use the sense of expanding your awareness outside of your body (p51) and notice what you experience. Try also making instant decisions about how you run your route. Play games with yourself by spontaneously running in a different direction, jogging backwards for a few steps or going in a zigzag across a path, changing direction in an instant. Each time you alter something, feel exactly where you are and what you're doing, continually tuning in to the new experience of now, and now, and now...

5 Take to the trails

Running off-road instantly requires you to be more mindful. Uneven ground, protruding tree roots or simply feeling your way along a footpath in the height of summer when hedgerows are at their most lush are all you need you to be much more attentive to your surroundings. If you usually train on the pavement or at the gym, explore what it feels like to run on grass, a woodland track or along the banks of a river. Start slowly, initially using your sense of sight to pick out a safe path ahead. With a soft focus, allow your eyes to take in the subtle shades of green that surround you, the different structural shapes of grass, shrubs and trees as you pass them by. Notice the speed at which objects appear to draw closer to you, seemingly speeding up as they pass directly at your side. After a few moments, take your attention to your feet and tune in to their sensitivity, feeling the micro-adjustments you need to make to maintain your balance as you tread on stones or a clump of grass. Breathe deeply, letting the fresh air permeate every cell as you feel your body expand to receive it – maintain your stride as you feel a sense of surrendering to the earth beneath you as you slowly and mindfully exhale. Savour every breath.

GO WITH
the flow

Whether it's in a pool or the open air, swimming mindfully is the perfect soothing meditation

*I*f you're a confident, experienced swimmer, you can practise mindful swimming with any stroke, but for most people, breast stroke is ideal to begin with as the technique allows you to glide through the water in a slow and conscious way. As with other mindfulness practices, bring your attention to your current-moment thoughts, feelings and bodily sensations. And, because breathing is such an integral aspect of swimming – your breath and body are co-ordinated in each stroke – you can use your breath to anchor you in the present moment. Here are some suggestions to get you started.

1 As you get into the pool, give your attention to the feel of the water as it touches your toes and gradually creeps up your legs. Is it warmer than the air temperature or cooler? Notice the effect on your upper body temperature as your lower body becomes submerged. Do the hairs on your arms stand up? Does your stomach contract at the anticipation of cold water? Take your time observing the minute sensations in your body, noticing if they bring any thoughts with them, any expectations. There's nothing to judge or to change, simply become aware of your experience as it is happening.

2 Once you're in the pool, pause for a few moments, and observe how it feels right now. Can you feel the movement of water around you? Do you sense its buoyancy, the lightness of your body? Take a few steps and feel the resistance around your legs and arms as you move through the water.

3 When you are ready to start swimming, come to the edge of the pool and prepare yourself to push off from the side. Stretch your arms in front of you and kick away, gliding forwards with your head submerged and your body fully extended. Feel the exhilaration of stretching from your fingertips to your toes, the sensuousness of the water rippling over your skin as you glide effortlessly forwards, the peacefulness that comes from being in perfect harmony with the water that carries you.

4 When you come to the end of your natural breath, raise your head and start to swim at a slow, comfortable pace. Feel the resistance of the water in your cupped palms as you first separate your palms, and the pressure on the sides of your body as you push the water behind you with your hands. Enjoy that moment of suspension with your arms outstretched as you glide through the water once more. Notice when the sense of propulsion ends and you need to separate your hands again in order to maintain momentum.

5 Now take your attention to your legs. Feel the instant surge forwards as you frog-leg your knees out sideways. Can you sense the simultaneous release in your hips? Synchronising your breath with your movements, feel your body working as a fluid, harmonious unit. Enjoy every sensation, fine-tuning your movements to respond to your body's needs.

6 When you come to the end of the pool, rest if you need to and then mindfully turn around and push off to swim back in the other direction.

7 After a length or two, using the techniques you've learnt in this book, such as abdominal breathing (p32), see if you can slow your pace even more, making two or three arm strokes to each in-breath. Each time you notice a thought arising, bring your attention back to your breath and your body.

INTO THE *wild*

You don't have to restrict your swimming to the local pool. Swimming in the open air can be deeply calming. Just 15 minutes in the deep velvety waters of a lake can leave you feeling peaceful and refreshed. As you step out of the water, your body feels grounded, your spirit light and your muscles as if they've just had a deep tissue massage. Add the wind rustling in the trees, the open sky above, gently swaying reeds – with the occasional passing duck! – and you're left with a sense of serenity that's difficult to replicate.

BACK TO NATURE

Wild swimming has become increasingly popular over recent years, and there are new locations emerging all the time. When you're surrounded by the beauty of nature, it's likely that swimming mindfully will come naturally to you, but focusing on the techniques above will help you attune to your body when your mind starts to wander.

If you're not a strong swimmer, just being in natural waters can be equally magical. It's a wonderful experience to simply stand in a river, feeling your feet on the riverbed while its current ripples through your fingertips. Resting for a while under a small waterfall gives you a unique moment-by-moment experience as the never-ending cascade of water showers down over you. In the sea, stand chest height in the salt water, facing the ocean, and notice if you

*When you're surrounded
by the beauty of nature,
it's likely that swimming
mindfully will come
naturally to you*

feel the energy of the waves in your belly – the water itself has to circumnavigate you, but some of its energy will simply travel through your body.

Most importantly, remember to stay safe. Natural waters are powerful and can be unpredictable. Never swim alone, cover open wounds, check the tides and talk to locals about any currents to look out for. If you're swimming in a river, throw a stick into the water, and if it moves faster than you can swim, give it a miss. Finally, avoid freshwater lakes with blue/green algae as it can irritate your skin and eyes, and make you ill if swallowed. You can find tips on wild swimming sites at wildswimming.co.uk.

SLOW TIPS

Simplify things: place a buoyancy aid between your outstretched arms and focus only on your leg movements, or between your thighs to give undivided attention to your arms.

Be single minded: focus on one experience at a time, such as the bubbles escaping from your mouth/nose as you exhale, or the movement of your shoulder blades as your extend and circle your arms.

Let it go: exhale through your nose to lengthen your out-breath, or purse your lips and blow gently through your mouth.

Conserve energy: if you get tired, swim a length on your back, using breast stroke legs and small 'scooping' motions with your hands.

STRETCH
it out

As you practise these poses, pay attention to the moment-by-moment sensations you experience, to help you stay in the present

If you're feeling stressed, overwhelmed or out of touch with who you deeply are, yoga is a wonderful way to come back home to yourself and the present moment, whatever it holds.

One of the definitions of yoga is to yoke or unite the mind and body. When we're preoccupied with thoughts or strong emotions, we can often feel a sense of separation both from others and ourselves. Being aware what your body is feeling, co-ordinating your breath with movement and taking care of your physical needs as you practise yoga can help begin to dissolve these barriers.

Some of the poses on the next few pages may already be familiar to you, but to bring a mindful quality to your practice, give your attention to the moment-by-moment sensations you experience as you work with the postures.

Breathing gently and fully into your belly throughout your practice, let yourself be curious about any areas of tension you feel and any discomfort, numbness or heat. Notice also your thoughts. Are you trying hard to get everything right? Do you feel competitive – even if only with yourself? See if you can simply observe your thoughts without judgement. Be sensitive also to any feelings the postures bring forward. Some people experience anger after a few breaths in Warrior II, for example, or as you rest deeply in Child's pose or Relaxation pose you may find that some sadness emerges.

Work with the postures in a way that feels right for you on the day you practise. Everyone has a unique anatomy, history of exercise and relationship to their body, so it's important you find your own expression of the pose. Honour the wisdom of your body and let it be your guide.

When you finish your practice, whether you're working on one pose or have completed the whole sequence, move with sensitivity as you continue on to the next phase of your day, so you don't disturb the atmosphere you've created and can keep the sense of relaxation.

Finally, rather than view the postures as fixed entities that have to look a certain way, see them as tools to help you find a deeper contact with yourself. As you come closer to that point of stillness in the centre of a pose, you may also find new insights arising that give you a deeper understanding of who you are and, with that, permission to treat yourself with greater kindness. Enjoy the journey.

THE
MOVES

Spend a minimum of five to 10 breaths in each pose, unless otherwise stated, but trust your inner guidance and follow what feels right for your body today

01 EASY SEATED POSE

✢ Sit on your mat and cross your legs, shins parallel to its front edge.
✢ Flex your feet, place your fingertips beside your hips and root through your sitting bones as you draw your navel to your spine and lengthen out of your pelvis.
✢ Open your chest, draw your shoulder blades down your back and lift through the crown of your head. Lengthen the back of your neck and close your eyes.
✢ Explore movement in your upper body by stretching your fingers, circling your wrists and shoulders, moving your arms in any way that feels natural to you and stretching and twisting your spine.
✢ Bring your hands to your thighs, palms upwards and weight sinking into the floor on each exhale. Let your mind be still.
✢ Breathe evenly into your belly for a few moments, then gently open your eyes.

02 EXTENDED CHILD'S POSE

✢ Kneel on your mat with your knees apart, big toes together, heels apart. On an exhale, walk your hands forwards, shoulder-width apart, and lower your torso between your thighs.
✢ Root your hands into the floor, keep your elbows off the mat and slide your shoulder blades down your back. Exhale and gently rest your forehead on the floor or a block. Softly close your eyes.
✢ Breathe deeply into your back body, extending through to your fingertips as you reach your tailbone to your heels.
✢ Walk your hands to your right, breathing into your left side. Take two breaths, then exhale your hands back to centre and repeat on the other side.
✢ On an exhale, use your hands to gently come up to a vertical spine.

03 CAT/COW

✢ Come on to all-fours, knees below your hips and wrists beneath your shoulders. Spread your fingers wide.
✢ Inhale, then, as you exhale, root through the base of your index fingers and thumbs as you release your head and tailbone to the floor and arc your spine to the ceiling. This is Cat pose (A).
✢ On your next inhale, tilt your tailbone upwards and release your spine down into a gentle backbend. Draw your shoulders down your back, take your chest forwards and up and gently raise your head. This is Cow pose (B).
✢ Alternate between Cat and Cow, instigating the movement from your pelvis and following the natural pattern of your breath. To make it freeflow, circle your hips, rotate your neck and snake the spine as feels good for your body.

04 THREAD THE NEEDLE

✦ Start on all-fours, as for Cat/Cow pose (no 3). Inhale as you lift your left arm up to the ceiling and rotate your torso so you're looking up at your left hand (A).
✦ As you exhale, lower your left hand and thread it beneath your chest and under your right shoulder (B).
✦ Bend your right elbow, lower your hips a little and bring the left side of your head or face to rest on the mat. Root into your right fingertips to take your shoulder back and deepen the twist. Take a couple of breaths here, then on your next inhale, unthread your hand and take it back overhead.
✦ Repeat the move twice more, then swap sides.

05 DOWNWARD-FACING DOG

✦ Begin on all-fours, hands a palm's length in front of your shoulders, shoulder-width apart, fingers spread.
✦ Root through the base of your thumbs and index fingers, then raise your knees, drawing your tailbone back and up.
✦ Keep your knees bent, initially, and focus on extending your spine by grounding through your hands. Rotate your upper arms externally and draw your shoulder blades down your spine. Lower your front ribs toward your thighs.
✦ Take a couple of breaths here, then gently draw one heel after the other towards the mat, in a walking motion. Spread your toes and, if possible, lower both heels. Experiment with freeflow yoga, for example, by making a figure of eight with your hips.

06 STANDING FORWARD FOLD

✦ From Mountain pose (no 7), with your feet hip-distance apart (A), take your hands to your hips and, on an inhale, root through your feet to lengthen your spine.
✦ Exhale, bend your knees slightly and fold forwards from your hips to a parallel spine. Keeping your knees bent, inhale to lengthen your spine once more, then, as you exhale, continue folding forwards. Release your arms and rest your hands on your ankles or the floor (B).
✦ On each in-breath, feel your spine lengthening; on each out-breath, fold a little deeper. Consciously surrender, breathing softly for several breaths.
✦ Make it freeflow, by swaying your arms side to side, perhaps bending one knee at a time as you swing to each side. Inhale and gently uncurl to standing.

07 EXTENDED MOUNTAIN POSE

✦ Place your feet together or up to shoulder-width apart, inner edges parallel. Balance your weight evenly over each foot. Spread your toes and root through the base of your big and little toes. Lift your inner arches by drawing your ankles away from each other.

✦ Draw your leg muscles to the bones, align your pelvis over your feet, relax your buttocks and allow your tail and sitting bones to release to the floor. Breathe.

✦ As you inhale, extend your arms to the sides and overhead, palms facing. As you exhale, release your shoulders down your spine.

✦ On each inhale, ground through your feet and feel the corresponding lift in your spine as you lengthen through to the crown of your head. On each exhale, visualise your breath travelling down your body and through your feet.

✦ Keep your gaze soft, and take five deep breaths, releasing your arms on an exhale to come out of the pose.

08 LOW LUNGE

✦ From Wide-legged standing forward fold (no 12), feet hip-width apart, place your hands either side of your feet and take a large step back with your right leg. Resting on the ball of your right foot, straighten your leg and extend through your back heel. Your left knee is directly over your ankle, aligned with your middle toes.

✦ Draw your left hip back and your right hip forwards to square your pelvis, then bring your thighs towards the mid-line.

✦ Lengthen through the crown of your head and draw your shoulder blades down your back, keeping your gaze a few feet in front of you on the floor. Breathe.

✦ To make it free-flow, draw your abdomen to your spine, and come up to a vertical spine, then explore moving your arms, one at a time, in large circles, extending them to the sides as you twist your torso to the right and left.

✦ Repeat on the other side.

09 SIDE ANGLE

✦ Step your feet a leg's distance apart, your left foot out 90°, your right foot in 15°. Align your front heel with your right instep, and root through the outer edge of your right foot.

✦ With your weight balanced between both feet, inhale to raise your arms to the sides, shoulder height, parallel to the floor and palms down.

✦ Exhale, bend your left knee over your ankle, keeping a micro-bend in your right leg as you take your left forearm to your thigh.

✦ Tilt your tailbone towards your back heel and rotate your chest open. Then, on an inhale, sweep your right arm alongside your ear, palm down.

✦ Ground through the outer edge of your back foot and feel the stretch from your toes to your fingertips. Gaze at the floor or, if comfortable, your upper hand. Breathe evenly and deeply.

✦ Pause for a moment before repeating on the other side.

⑩ WARRIOR II

✢ Step your feet a leg's distance apart, your left foot out 90°, your right foot in 15°. Align your front heel with your right instep, spread your toes and root through your big and little toes and the outside edge of your right foot.

✢ With your weight balanced between both feet, your pelvis in neutral and facing the long edge of your mat, inhale to raise your arms to the sides, shoulder height, parallel to the floor and palms down. Lengthen from your centre to beyond your fingertips.

✢ On an exhale, bend your left leg to take your knee directly over your ankle, keeping a micro-bend in your right leg.

✢ Breathing evenly, draw your navel to your spine, open your chest and slide your shoulders down your spine. If comfortable, turn your head to gaze along your front arm, beyond your middle finger.

✢ Pause for a moment before repeating on the other side.

⑪ REVERSE WARRIOR

✢ From Warrior II (no 10), inhale as you slide your back arm down your back thigh, and raise your front arm overhead, gently arching your spine laterally.

✢ Root your feet down and lift your torso up on each inhale, feeling your side body open and, as you exhale, arc a little further into the back bend. If comfortable for your neck, gaze at your upper hand, otherwise, look forwards and slightly upwards.

✢ Take five deep breaths in the pose, then, on an exhale, lower your top arm and straighten your front leg.

✢ Pause for a moment before repeating on the other side.

⑫ WIDE-LEGGED STANDING FORWARD FOLD

✢ Step your feet wide, inner edges parallel, toes spread and arches lifted. Anchor the outer edges of your feet.

✢ Rest your hands on your hips and, on an inhale, root through your feet to lengthen your spine. As you exhale, fold forwards from your hips with a flat back, to take your spine horizontal to the floor.

✢ Bring your arms behind your back and interlace your fingers, then continue lengthening your spine as you inhale, folding deeper as you exhale, bringing your arms up and forwards over your head.

✢ For a more restful variation, place your hands on the floor beneath your shoulders, forearms vertical, head releasing to the floor.

✢ Breathe deeply and evenly for five to 10 breaths then, taking your hands back to your hips, inhale to come back up to standing.

⑬ TREE

✢ From standing, transfer your weight onto your left leg. Spread your toes and ground through the base of the big and little toes. Lift the inner arch.

✢ Keeping a micro-bend in your supporting knee, focus on a fixed point ahead and place the sole of your right foot against your inner left thigh or calf. Use your right hand to lift your foot if needed, then place your hands on your hips.

✢ Breathing into your belly, press the sole of your right foot into your left thigh and engage your thigh to anchor your foot. Draw your tailbone towards the floor and your belly to your spine. Root through your supporting leg as you lengthen your spine through to your crown.

✢ Bring your hands to prayer position and take three to five breaths then exhale and gently lower your hands and foot. Pause for a moment before repeating on the other side.

⑭ GARLAND

✢ With your feet wider than hip-width apart, inhale then, on an exhale, gently crouch down into a low squat, taking your hands to the floor in front of you. Turn your feet out, so your knees are over your toes, then lower your heels, taking your feet as far apart as needed so your heels anchor into the ground.

✢ Lift your hands into prayer position and let your tailbone release to the mat. Press your palms together as you root through your feet, and push your upper arms into your inner thighs, your thighs into your arms. This will help you lift out of your pelvis to lengthen through your spine.

✢ Draw your shoulder blades down your back and let your chest expand. Take five to 10 deep breaths into your belly.

✢ When you're ready to come out, release your hands and come to a comfortable seated position.

⑮ HEAD-TO-KNEE FORWARD FOLD

✢ Sit with your legs extended then fold your right leg in so your heel touches your pubic bone and the sole rests on your inner thigh. Draw your left hip back and your right knee forwards to square your hips. Flex your left ankle, reaching through the ball of your foot, and draw your navel to your spine.

✢ Inhale as you raise your arms overhead, palms facing, then, on an exhale, lead with the crown of your head to fold forwards from your hips, taking your chest to your left thigh and your hands to your shin, ankle or sole of the foot.

✢ Inhale again to lengthen, then exhale and fold a little further forwards, keeping the front body long. When you reach your edge, release your head down towards your left knee.

✢ Breathe evenly and deeply for two minutes, enjoying the sensation of surrender. Inhale to come up to sitting and repeat on the other side.

16 SEATED TWIST

✦ From sitting with your legs extended, place your right foot outside your left knee, toes forwards and right knee pointing to the ceiling. Bend your left knee and slide your right foot to the outside of your left hip. Root through your sitting bones.

✦ Rest your right hand behind you and on an inhale raise your left hand. As you exhale, take your elbow outside your left knee, forearm vertical and palm facing the right. Keep your spine vertical and draw your shoulder blades into your back.

✦ Inhale as you root through your right hand and sitting bones to lengthen your spine, then as you exhale, twist to the right. Move a little deeper into the stretch with each breath. Take your time, listening to the cues your body is giving you.

✦ Inhale to gently ease back to the centre, then pause before repeating on the other side.

17 BRIDGE

✦ Lie on your back and take a moment to arrive in your body, then bend your knees and place your feet hip-distance apart and parallel, directly beneath your knees. Rest your arms at your sides, palms down.

✦ Inhale, ground through your feet and, on an exhale, tilt your tailbone up to gently peel your spine away from the floor, vertebra by vertebra.

✦ Keep your thighs parallel, knees hip-distance apart and continue rooting through your feet to lift your chest. Roll your shoulders up, back and down, then lengthen the back of your neck.

✦ Bring your hands together beneath you, interlink your fingers and snuggle your shoulders together. Focus on grounding through your feet to lift through your heart.

✦ Take five deep breaths into your abdomen, then, on an exhale, slowly uncurl your spine to rest on the floor. Extend one leg at a time, then rest for a few moments with your eyes closed.

18 RELAXATION POSE

✦ Lie on your back, legs a comfortable distance apart, arms to the sides of your body, palms facing the ceiling. Gently close your eyes.

✦ Breathe softly and evenly into your belly, letting your eyelids be heavy, and your eyes sink deeper into their sockets. Relax your temples and soften your jaw. Release your neck, shoulders and arms. Invite your belly to expand and your thighs, calves and ankles to relax. Let everything be soft and heavy.

✦ Rest for five to 10 minutes. Breathe naturally, allowing your body to experience a sense of expansion as you inhale, and a feeling of softening as you exhale.

✦ To come out of the pose, slowly wriggle your fingers and toes then gently stretch your body from your feet to your fingertips. Slowly bring your knees to your chest, roll over to your right side and rest for few moments, then use your left hand to help you come up to sitting.

THE
SEQUENCE

Spend a minimum of five to 10 breaths in each pose, unless otherwise stated, but trust your inner guidance and follow what feels right for your body today

01 Easy seated pose
p80
Come onto your knees and sit back into...

02 Extended child's pose
p80
Come onto all fours, into

03 Cat/Cow F
p80
Move straight into

04 Thread the needle
p81
Take your hands shoulder-width apart and raise your hips into

05 Downward-facing dog F
p81
Walk your feet forwards into

06 Standing forward fold F
p81
On an in-breath, take your arms out to the side and overhead as you come up to

07 Extended mountain pose
p82
On an out-breath, take your arms out to the side as you lower your hands either side of your feet and step your right leg back into

08 Low lunge F
p82
Turn your back toes under and place your right foot parallel to the short end of your mat. Place your left hand inside your left foot (or your forearm on your left thigh) and arc your right arm overhead to come into

09 Side angle
p82
Bring both arms parallel to the floor to come into

10 Warrior II
p83
Slide your right hand down your thigh and raise your left arm overhead into

11 Reverse warrior
p83
Come back up to Warrior II, then turn your feet to parallel and lower into

12 Wide-legged standing forward fold
p83
Walk your hands to your right foot and repeat 9-12 on the other side. Walk your hands to your left foot, turn to face the front of your mat and come up to standing.

13 Tree
p84
Balance for a few breaths on each leg, then lower into

14 Garland
p84
Lower onto your bottom, then bring your left leg in front of you to come into

15 Head-to-knee forward fold
p84
Place your right foot outside your left knee to come into

16 Seated twist
p85
Release and repeat 15-16 on the other side

17 Bridge
p85

18 Relaxation pose
p85

✳ FREE-FLOW YOGA
Where a pose is marked with **F** explore any movement in it that feels good. If you feel your body could benefit from revisiting certain postures, repeat them before moving onto the next one. You could also alternate between consecutive postures a few times to build a mindful flow. Poses 6 & 7 and 9, 10 & 11 work well in this way.

FINISH

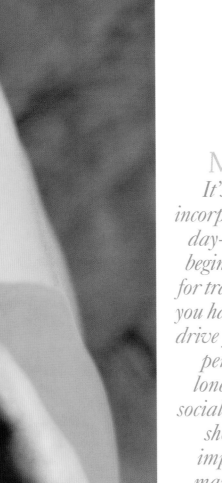

EVERYDAY MINDFULNESS

It's only when you begin to incorporate mindfulness into your day-to-day life that you really begin to appreciate its potential for transforming your life. Maybe you have a demanding job yet still drive yourself to achieve more. Or perhaps you sometimes feel lonely, despite having a wide social circle. In this chapter, we'll show you mindful ways to improve your relationships, manage work stress and ease physical pain. If you want to lose weight, the mindful eating strategies will help you better understand your relationship with food, and if you'd like some inspiration for making every moment mindful, the last two chapters – Build your own refuge and Pocket mindfulness – are packed with ideas!

MINDFUL
MEALS

Paying attention to the experience of
eating and drinking is a useful tool in
your mindfulness practice

That explosion of
flavour when you
bite into a crisp,
juicy apple... the
delicious tingling
as salted-caramel
chocolate melts in your mouth...
a glass of ice-cold water on a
scorching summer's day... When it
comes to eating, nothing beats the
joy of taking that first bite into a
much-anticipated delight – but once the
initial burst of flavour subsides, the
intensity of your experience inevitably
diminishes, fading to mild satisfaction at
best; cloying, dull or repetitive at worst.

The reason nothing quite matches the
sheer joy of that first bite is, largely,
because we're no longer as attentive to
our moment-to-moment experience. We
don't maintain that sense of freshness,
wonder and awe of a beginner's mind.
Just imagine how your food would taste
if you were able to sustain the same level

of attention and experience as in your
first bite. Just imagine how your life
would look if you were fully present with
all your senses in each moment.

Mindful eating involves paying full
attention to the experience of eating
and drinking, both inside and outside
your body, and, as a sensation-rich
experience, it's great training in
mindfulness practice. When you eat
consciously, you notice the colours,
flavours, smells and textures of your
food. You become attentive to the
sounds it makes as you chew. You
bring your awareness to the responses
in your body, the emotions you feel and
the thoughts that arise. You observe
what it feels like to experience hunger
and satisfaction.

The raisin exercise (p44) is the
traditional introduction to mindful eating.
Once you have tried it, you might like
to move on to some of the practices over
the page. Bon appetite!

DRINK UP

Take the first few sips of your morning tea or coffee with complete awareness. Where in your mouth can you feel its heat? How far can you sense it travelling down your oesophagus? Can you tell on which part of your tongue the taste lingers? Notice the difference drinking like this makes to your sense of thirst and your feelings of satiety.

CHECK IN

In the course of your meal, rest your awareness on your stomach and notice how it is feeling. Buddhist monks will regularly check in with their stomachs as they eat, asking if they are a quarter full, half full, three-quarters full, over full. Mindful eating can help avoid overeating and unnecessary weight gain.

SWAP HANDS

Eat a meal with one hand, holding your fork in your left hand if you're right-handed, and vice versa if you're left-handed. Eating more slowly will help you become more conscious of the food you're tasting. And as an added bonus, if you're trying to lose weight, research shows you'll eat 30 per cent less if you eat with your non-dominant hand.

APPRECIATE YOUR MEAL

As you eat, reflect on the journey your food has travelled to get to your plate. The farmer who ploughed the field, the seasonal worker who harvested it, the packers, drivers and distributors. The fisherman who was awake 72 hours catching that mackerel, right down to the person who went to work (perhaps you) to pay for the ingredients. As you begin to appreciate the many people involved in bringing food to your plate, you may feel a sense of gratitude, and an appreciation for the way we are all, in fact, connected.

HOLD THE TALK

Have you ever eaten a meal in silence? Refraining from talking can acutely attune you to many levels of experience. As well as enabling you to appreciate your food more, it's a great way to experience being present without the pressure to be anything other than who you are. Seeing and being truly seen can bring greater self-acceptance and increase feelings of acceptance of your friend/relation. It also teaches you to be mindful when you're with others, as opposed to being alone. If it sounds a bit daunting, try it for just five minutes at the beginning of your meal. Using a Tibetan bell timer is a beautiful way to mark the opening and closure of the meditation, and the formality of the bell helps to remove any sense of self-consciousness. Try it with the Insight Timer app (p37).

JUST EAT

If you tend to eat while you're reading, online, working or watching TV, try alternating these activities. For example, read a page, then put the book down and eat a few mouthfuls, savouring the tastes, smells and textures, then read another page, and so on. Notice how different this feels from doing both activities at the same time. Try it with a salad or a sandwich, so you don't get anxious about your food getting cold before you eat it.

CHEW THOROUGHLY

Try chewing each mouthful 30 times or more before swallowing it. Not only does

this ease stress-related digestive symptoms, it also gives you ample time to tune to all your bodily sensations, thoughts and emotions. At first, it might seem laborious, but you'll soon notice the calming affect it has on your system. The act of counting will help keep you focused on the present moment, and you'll soon know if your mind has wandered when you forget what number you're on.

COOK SLOWLY

Find an afternoon or evening when you're not pushed for time and ban electric gadgets in favour of chopping, slicing, whisking and mashing by hand.

Use a stoneware pestle and mortar to grind spices and pick herbs or edible flowers from your garden or window box. Each time you add a new ingredient to your dish, tune in to your body and ask it how much it needs today. Taste your creation often, and notice the subtle changes the addition has made. Let your cooking become a mindful art.

SET THE SCENE

Instead of saving it for a special occasion – life is the special occasion – set the table with beautiful plates and cutlery, even if you are eating alone. In fact, especially if you are eating alone. Using your favourite cup and saucer and laying

a beautiful table feeds your senses, bringing a quality of reverence and ritual to your meal, and so nourishes your body, mind and soul.

START SMALL

Make a decision to eat more mindfully and stick to it for one month. Be realistic about what you're able to fit in and, whether it's one meal a week, one meal a day, one bite in every meal or every time you eat something green, do your best to honour your commitment to yourself. Keep a record of your experiences in your mindfulness journal and notice what progress you make.

Chew each mouthful 30 times. Not only does this ease stress-related digestive symptoms, it also gives you time to tune into your bodily sensations, thoughts and emotions

IMPROVE YOUR
relationships

Bring clarity to your relationships
with this enlightening exercise

The deep sense of contentment that comes from being in a successful relationship is something we all long for. Indeed, loving and being loved is a basic human need. But relationships aren't always easy. With its focus on being fully present, compassionate and non-judgemental, it's no surprise that mindfulness brings an emotional richness to our personal life, but it also works on a physiological level. Research shows mindfulness strengthens a part of the brain associated with cognitive flexibility (the anterior cingulate cortex) – affecting your ability to see problems from a different perspective. It also has a calming influence on the amygdala, the area of the brain that alerts you to perceived threat – both physical or emotional. The result? You're less likely to be plagued with relationship insecurities if you practise mindfulness.

All the exercises in this book will teach you how to become more conscious in your relationships and help you manage moments of conflict, but the RAIN exercise on the next two pages is particularly useful in helping you gain clarity about what you're feeling in situ. Adapted from the Buddhist practice known as Vipassanā, it will also help you begin to unravel the sometimes complex and intertwined threads of your history that have brought you to your current experience.

The next time you find yourself in an emotionally challenging situation, remember the acronym RAIN and give this exercise a try. The more you work with it, the more skillful you will become in recognising the truth of your experience and the more able you'll be to respond in a conscious, honest and appropriate way.

RECOGNISE

The first step in understanding conflict in a relationship is to be aware of what you're bringing to the interaction, and you may find there are several layers. For example, if your partner expects more than you can give, you may feel guilty for not meeting his wishes, while at the same time resenting him for making what you believe are unreasonable demands. Perhaps you also feel hurt that nothing you do seems good enough, yet also feel compassion towards yourself for trying so hard. Initially, all you need to do is notice your feelings. Nothing more.

It can be helpful to name them, for example,' I feel pressured' or 'I feel misunderstood'. Also, be aware of any thoughts that arise, such as 'Maybe I'm just being selfish' or 'He *always* expects more, why does he never see my point of view?'

ACCEPT

The next stage is to work on accepting what you're feeling and thinking. This isn't always that easy, as most of us have been taught there are certain thoughts and emotions we simply shouldn't express or, indeed, feel.

Instead of taking on other people's interpretations of what is appropriate for you, allow yourself to become open to the fact that these are the emotions you are feeling today. And that is fine. They are simply there. It may help to remember that no thought or feeling is 'wrong'. Even unwanted or unpleasant emotions are valuable doorways into a deeper understanding of yourself.

*I*NVESTIGATE

Next, bring an open-minded curiosity to your feelings. Put aside for the moment thoughts of who's to blame or what you might want to do about the situation. And begin to delve deeper into what you're experiencing. You might ask yourself if you can sense the emotion in your body, or if you have ever felt this way before.

Using the example above, you might perhaps remember that your father also expected more of you than you felt able to give. Or that guilt is an emotion you regularly feel. By exploring your emotions with non-judgemental inquisitiveness, you may find some new insights into how you behave in close relationships.

*N*NON-IDENTIFICATION

In the final stage of RAIN, while you may still be feeling the emotion of, say, rejection, you choose not to identify with it. You acknowledge the feeling is present, but you don't let it define you.

In this way you don't become a person who has been rejected – and all the attendant thoughts and feelings that can go with that notion – but someone who experienced the emotion of rejection. This can be a deeply liberating experience, and one that allows you to bring a calmer, wiser way of relating to people you are in conflict with..

Once you're familiar with the RAIN technique, use it to help reduce stress and bring focus to any situation.

THE ROAD LESS TRAVELLED

Do you ever kick yourself for making the same mistake twice? Maybe you always choose to date an emotionally unavailable man. Or perhaps you find yourself 'mothering' someone yet again. Some psychologists might say we're choosing partners that trigger our childhood emotional issues, with the hope that by encountering the problem as an adult we have a better chance of resolving it. There are other times, though, when we simply need to change the way we relate to others. This poem sums up the journey perfectly. And the more mindful you become, the sooner you reach the last chapter.

There's A Hole In My Sidewalk: Autobiography In Five Short Chapters by Portia Nelson

Chapter I
I walk down the street.
There is a deep hole in
the sidewalk.
I fall in.
I am lost... I am helpless.
It isn't my fault.
It takes forever to find
a way out.

Chapter II
I walk down the
same street.
There is a deep hole in
the sidewalk.
I pretend I don't see it.
I fall in again.
I can't believe I am in the
same place.
But, it isn't my fault.
It still takes a long time
to get out.

Chapter III
I walk down the
same street.
There is a deep hole in
the sidewalk.
I see it is there.
I still fall in... it's a habit.
But, my eyes are open.
I know where I am.
It is my fault.
I get out immediately.

Chapter IV
I walk down the
same street.
There is a deep hole in
the sidewalk.
I walk around it.

Chapter V
I walk down
another street.

Mindfulness
AT WORK

Use mindfulness techniques to increase
your productivity, get on better with
colleagues and enjoy your job

*I*n 2015/16, a shocking 45 per cent of all sick days taken in the UK were attributed to stress, according to the Health & Safety Executive, with tight deadlines, workload pressures and too much responsibility being the main culprits. Of course, some people thrive on pressure, and while you may think people are either naturally resilient or not, surprisingly perhaps, resilience is a skill you can learn.

Mindfulness techniques can go a long way to helping you manage work-related stress better, improve your communication skills, increase productivity and, most importantly, be more compassionate towards yourself, teaching you to accept what you can't change about a situation. Sometimes, for instance, acceptance is all it takes for you to realise that a role is not for you, and that it's time to move on. On the other hand, if a problem at work does arise, and you're in a relaxed, mindful state of being, your creativity has free rein to come up with an often unusual or overlooked solution to the problem. The result? You end up enjoying your job far more. Read on to learn how to feel more comfortable and confident at work.

IT'S GOOD TO TALK

One of the key ways to benefit from mindfulness at work is through clearer communication. We've looked at communication skills in greater depth in mindfulness for relationships (p94), but in a professional context, the boundaries are different. When you're multi-tasking, working to tight deadlines or have several people making demands at the same time, it's easy to be distracted and only take in part of what is being said to you. When the pressure's on, all too often we give an answer or opinion before we've fully absorbed the content or context of the discussion. Being present in a calm and centered manner means you can get to the essence of issues more swiftly, and reply in a more measured and complete way. To bring more mindfulness to your communication at work, follow these three steps:

LISTEN: Use centering skills (breathing into your belly, connecting to the ground beneath you, being aware of physical sensations in your body) to listen fully to what is being said. Allow the other person to finish what they're saying before you reply and, if needed, check that you have understood them correctly. For example, 'So, as I understand it, you'd like me to… Is that right?' Again, be as centered as you can as you give your answer.

CLARIFY: If there is a difference of opinion, acknowledge the issues that you agree on to create a common ground and sense of teamwork before going on to tackle any areas of difference.

COLLABORATE: Work as equals to find a mutually agreeable solution or compromise, listening fully and exploring all potential avenues. Being as mindful as you are able to be in the situation will help your creativity! Alternatively, you may have to respectfully accept that you disagree.

JUST A MINUTE

Whenever your work piles up and you feel the tension rising, take a moment to reconnect to a mindful state of being. First, connect to your breath. Take three deep, slow breaths, breathing right down to your abdomen, feel your weight sinking downwards as you do. Then take your awareness to your sitting bones (if you're seated), your legs and the floor. Finally, notice your thoughts. Without trying to change anything, simply observe them, accept them and let them go. When you feel ready, continue with your day. You may decide there's something you want to change. If so, follow what your new, mindful connection is saying that you need to do.

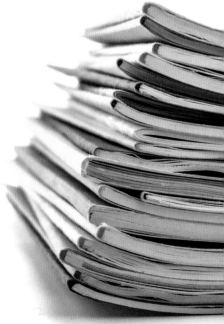

Breathe

COME BACK TO YOURSELF

Research by Harvard University shows up to 47 per cent of your day can be lost in mind-wandering! Remind yourself to return to a more mindful state of being with a Tibetan bell alarm on your mobile, an inspiring screensaver, a small post-it note with the word 'Breathe' or an inspiring object on your desk. I have a tiny bronze statue of Ganesh, the Indian God known as the 'remover of obstacles', but you can use whatever works for you – no one need know its purpose, as long as it serves to remind you to tune back into yourself. You could also use certain activities to remind you to check in with yourself, such as every time you take a sip of water, or when you begin a new task.

BODY SCAN 101

Few of us have the luxury of being able to do a body scan during the working day, so this quick body check is a useful tool for helping you identify areas of tension in your body. It only takes three to five minutes so you can do it at your desk, but if you can find a completely quiet area where you won't be disturbed, even better (perhaps you can book a meeting room for 15 minutes?).

Mentally divide your body into three areas – your pelvis, legs and feet; your chest and arms; your shoulders neck, head and face – then take your attention to each of them in turn, in the order listed, starting with your feet and travelling up your body. Become aware of any sensations you feel such as heat, cold, constriction, palpitations, tingling and numbness. Once you've registered the sensation, let it go on an outbreath and move on to the next area. Stay still for a few moments breathing into your belly to finish. Notice what you are feeling now.

HAVE A BREAK

Whether you've got too much to do or you've already done too much, when you are mentally stressed or exhausted, your work suffers. Known as the Yerkes-Dodson curve, your quality of performance rises and falls in relation to your level of alertness. There's a period after your optimal level of mental activity and quality of work performance called the zone of delusion. Here, stress and anxiety have kicked in, but you still think you're achieving your goals. But mistakes, poor quality of work and a wandering mind mean time spent in this zone is unproductive. The good news is that the sooner you realise this, the quicker you'll refresh your mind and return to peak productivity. As soon as you notice you're in the zone, do a mindfulness exercise to check what you need to do next. Connect with your breath, observe your thoughts and tune into your body, then ask yourself what you need to do such as eating food, getting fresh air or talking to a colleague.

TECHNOLOGY ADDICT?

Research shows the neurohormone dopamine causes 'seeking behaviour' – not just for the basic need for food, shelter or warmth, but for information also. When your need is met, by eating a meal, for example, your brain produces those feel-good opioids such as endorphine. When it comes to technology, if you're feeling low, the ping of a text, email or twitter feed will trigger dopamine release, so checking your computer/mobile feels imperative. And the shorter/more incomplete the message, the greater the dopamine release and the more compelled you feel to check for the latest update. Constant distraction from the task at hand is draining and compromises your focus. To stay productive and on task, turn the sound cues off your devices, and timetable when you'll check emails/messages and twitter feeds.

TAKE THREE

Do you feel your stress levels rise the minute your office phone rings? Or perhaps you leave it for the answering machine, all the while hoping it's not important? In his book *Peace is Every Step* (Rider, £9.99), Thich Naht Hahn suggests waiting for three rings before answering any phone. If it's urgent the caller will wait that long to speak to you or leave a message. And it means you can take three deep breaths to create space, not only to choose whether you want to take the call, but also to let go of what you've been doing and centre yourself in this new moment, so you can be fully present when you speak to the caller.

COMMUTING

Almost four million Brits spend two hours a day travelling to work, with the average being almost an hour. Add to this accidents and cancelled trains, and it's no surprise journeys can leave you feeling unmindful. Here are our tips for taking the stress out of your commute.

ACCEPT YOUR LOT

The fact that your travel time is unpredictable is a big stressor. The best way to manage the dis-ease is to accept there's nothing you can do to change it. Practise the mindful techniques in this book to minimise the stress and use the time to learn that language you've always wanted to speak or finish that report for your boss.

PRACTISE KINDNESS

Have mindful connections with your fellow travellers. Notice the difference to your mood and energy if you let a car go in front of you or offer your seat to someone. It will lift your mood, as your brain produces more endogenous opioids, which elevate levels of dopamine, so giving you a natural high.

FOCUS ATTENTION...

...on something other than the slowness of the journey. Notice other people's faces in the train. Observe your thoughts and feelings without judging them. Simply let them register then let them go, and notice the difference this has on your experience of the journey.

SUSPEND YOUR JUDGEMENT

Being contradicted or having someone disagree with your point of view can be challenging and when it happens in a big meeting with your entire team and line managers present, it's even tougher. Perhaps you go on the defensive and argue your case even more strongly, or perhaps you retreat into yourself, feeling a sense of shame or humiliation? Next time someone disagrees with you, use it as an opportunity to practise mindful breathing, and see if you can allow yourself to listen deeply to what your colleague is saying. Be curious, as if you were an impartial observer. Is she really saying her opinion is right and yours is wrong? Are there valuable elements to both points of view? Keep breathing into your belly as you listen, and use your sense of touch to stay grounded (p52) by feeling the seat of your chair and the floor beneath your feet. With practice and mindful self-acceptance there will come a time when, even if your colleague's opinion *is* 'better' than yours, it will make no difference to your sense of self worth.

BE THANKFUL

Gratitude diaries have become a hot trend in recent years, but don't just write down what you appreciate at the end of the day, tell co-workers how much you value their input. Being grateful and showing your appreciation for any help you receive benefits both parties. Not only will they feel valued, in giving yourself a voice and making your feelings known, you are also increasing your sense of presence in the workplace.

EASE YOUR
pain

Mindfulness doesn't just
soothe your mind, it
can relieve physical
discomfort too

Living with pain can
be a challenge.
Whether it's
exercise-induced
muscle stiffness or
a chronic condition with limited relief
from conventional treatment, pain
can bring a host of psychological
symptoms along with any physical
discomfort. When pain isn't well
managed, you may end up feeling
anxious, exhausted, sleep-deprived,
angry or even depressed. Of course,
any unexplained pain should always be
investigated by your health care provider,
but mindfulness techniques can go
a long way to helping mitigate your
experience of physical discomfort.

Traditionally, psychological approaches to pain management advocated limiting negative thought patterns associated with your condition. But a newer approach has emerged in recent years, encouraging you to view your condition with acceptance and to live as full and productive a life as possible – alongside your pain.

And it's not a grin-and-bear-it approach. In recent years, a growing body of research shows that mindfulness meditation doesn't just ease your thoughts and feelings about your condition, it also physically relieves pain by creating structural and functional changes in the brain.

NATURAL PAINKILLER

A study published in *The Journal of Neuroscience* showed that mindfulness reduces pain more effectively than placebos by activating the orbitofrontal cortex and the anterior cingulate cortex of the brain – regions linked with how you control your pain levels. In addition, the thalamas was deactivated, a

Growing research shows that mindfulness meditation physically relieves pain by creating structural and functional changes in the brain

structure above the brain stem that acts as a gateway to determine which sensory information reaches the higher brain centres. Another study by the University of Colorado Boulder found that brain pathways that contribute to your experience of pain can be self-regulated.

And it's not just meditation that can ease pain, regular yoga practice can help too. Dr Catherine Bushnell, scientific director at the National Center for Complementary and Integrative

Health (NIH), in Maryland, US, has been researching the impact of brain anatomy on pain reduction and she has found that changes in the grey matter in the cerebral cortex are the major players in chronic pain. Her research shows that yoga practitioners have more grey matter than control subjects in regions of the brain associated with pain modulation. If you don't already have a yoga practice, turn to p78 for some useful yoga postures to try.

EXERCISES TO TRY

The best way to work mindfully with pain is through a regular meditation practice, but the following exercises will help when your levels of discomfort rise

USE YOUR BREATH

After spending a few moments to become centred, begin to slowly direct your in-breath to an area of your body that's in pain. For example, if you have lower back pain, with your mind's eye, imagine your breath travelling from your nose, through your throat and into your chest, then to your abdomen to rest at your lower back. As you exhale, imagine your breath dissolving and expanding into the area and out beyond your skin surface. Visualise the tension and pain melting away on each exhale.

Repeat this pattern on the next and subsequent breaths for five to 10 minutes, then gently let go of the sequence and return to your normal breath for a few moments before opening your eyes. As you become familiar with the exercise, you might like to imagine your breath as a fine white light, travelling through your body and transforming into a soft gold as it reaches the area you're working with.

FEEL THE SENSATIONS

In this technique, you focus your attention on the sensations that make up your discomfort. Is the pain sharp or diffused? Is there heat? Cold? Do you feel any burning? Can you feel any throbbing or tingling? If you separate out the sensations you are experiencing – a technique known as 'sensory splitting' – you're less likely to view pain as a permanent thing, but see it more as a combination of different and constantly changing sensations. Be observant and curious about the sensations you're feeling, notice them arise, become stronger and begin to recede.

FOCUS ELSEWHERE

Spend some time giving your attention to a part of your body that is not in pain. Allow your awareness to rest in that area and tune in to the sensations you feel there. Maybe there is warmth, a sense of strength or fluidity. See if you can relax into the sensations and allow them to be the dominant ones you feel. This exercise is helpful in showing you that pain isn't the only feeling you can contact in your body. You can explore movement in these areas, maybe enjoying the feeling of stretching your toes and rotating your ankle, feeling the freedom that this brings you.

DISTRACT YOURSELF

Notice as many other sensory experiences as you can in this moment. A gentle breeze on your skin as you sit by an open window, the colour of the sunlight as it reflects on your kitchen floor, the sound of birdsong, a passing car or your children playing in another room. When you flood your body and mind with other sensory inputs, your pain may lessen as it becomes just one sensation amid a group of many that you are experiencing in the present moment.

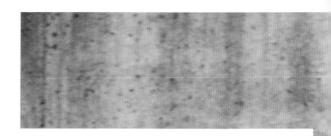

Mindfulness
FOR FITNESS

Adopt a mindful approach to your workouts and you could enhance your sports performance

As the trend for mindfulness expands into more areas of life, specific applications emerge, and fitness is no exception. In the past, if you wanted to optimise your training sessions, improve your performance or reach your fitness goals, you may have employed traditional sports psychology techniques such as goal-setting, self-talk or visualisations of sailing past the finishing line. Or you may have looked into sport-specific cognitive behaviour therapy (CBT), which takes the view that any negative thought or emotion must be banished from your mind if you are to perform at your best.

Recent studies suggest, however, that some of these techniques are not always consistent in their results, and can even have an opposite effect from the one desired. By trying to eliminate negative thoughts, for example, you can inadvertently end up focusing on these states of mind, not just increasing their frequency but also distracting yourself from your performance. Hardly the result you're aiming for! Instead, a better way to boost your sports performance can be to develop non-judgemental, present moment acceptance of your thoughts, feelings and bodily sensations. In other words, mindfulness.

PERFORMANCE BOOST

Research backs up this view. The first study to look at mindfulness-based interventions for athletes was in 1985 and it found that, after a period of mindfulness training, a group of rowers performed way above their coach's expectations, while several medal-winning Olympic rowers said the training had aided their performance. Fast-forward 20 years, and clinical psychologists Carol Glass and Keith Kaufman developed a programme to help fitness fans and athletes in their bid to meet their fitness goals. Called mindful sport performance enhancement (MSPE), the six-week course is adaptable to any sport, and uses many of the techniques in this book, including the raisin exercise (see p42), except that MSPE replaces the raisin with chocolate!), sitting meditations (increasing

Instead of having a rigid plan about what you should achieve with your weekly workouts, adopt a more flexible approach. It might just help you reach your goals quicker!

from 10-25 minutes over the duration of the course), breathing meditations, a body scan, mindful yoga, walking meditations and a sport-specific meditation, such as a running meditation. All these practices will help boost your sports performance, so turn to the relevant pages in this book to get your fitness back on track.

Here are some more ways mindfulness can enhance your sporting experience.

EMBRACE FLEXIBILITY

Mindfulness is about acceptance, and this relates to your training as well as your performance. So when it comes to your weekly workouts, instead of having a rigid plan about what you should achieve, adopt a more flexible approach. It might just help you reach your goals quicker! For example, if you're learning a yoga pose from a book or the internet, rather than tell yourself 'I must point my head in this direction' or 'I have to raise my leg to this height', say to yourself, 'One way to point my head might be…'

This subtle difference – an approach you could call mindful learning – has surprising effects, sports psychology research reveals. Participants taught to hit a ball with conditional language ('Try hitting it this way') rather than absolute language ('You must hold the bat like this'), were able to adapt their moves successfully and use different body parts when the researchers secretly replaced the ball with a heavier one. Those participants who were given specific instructions were much less able to adapt their moves to respond to the heavier ball.

GET IN THE ZONE

Imagine you're running a 10K. Your body feels balanced, your legs powerful and you've found your optimum pace – you

feel you could go on for ever, step by step, breath by breath, never tiring. Not a runner? Think of the last time you had a good swim. You're in the pool and your body is working in perfect harmony as you glide effortlessly through the water as if it's your natural habitat, breath co-ordinated and muscles poised in that sweet spot between tension and relaxation. There's nowhere else you'd rather be.

Peak-performance experiences, also known as being in the zone, are associated with what sports psychologists refer to as states of flow – those times when you feel able to meet the challenges of the sporting situation you face. It's actually a very mindful state – you're so involved in what you're doing, enjoying it so much that nothing else matters. Your mind and body are in harmony and you have no self-doubt. Some researchers would say this state leads to optimal sport performance. And there's good evidence to show a strong connection between mindfulness and

states of flow in athletes. In fact, studies show that after mindfulness-based exercises, sports people have a significant increase in their 'levels of flow'.

BEAT PERFORMANCE ANXIETY

Do you get anxious before a big event? Perhaps you're taking on a cycling challenge and feel nervous about whether you've done sufficient training. Or maybe a touch of anxiety impacts on your enjoyment when you try a sport for the first time or have to stand at the front of a yoga class.

MSPE has been shown to significantly reduce sport-related anxiety and boost levels of sport-related optimism. What's more, the benefits last! Twelve months after completing an MSPE workshop, participants in a 2011 trial were still experiencing the benefits, enjoying their sport more and reporting an increase in general satisfaction in their lives.

BUILD YOUR OWN *refuge*

Recharge your body and mind by creating a mini-mindfulness retreat at home

It's not always possible to get away for a meditation retreat, so why not set aside some time for a day of mindfulness practices? Whether you just want to take things at a slower pace or you'd like to work on a specific issue such as calming anxiety, repairing a relationship with a friend or becoming more conscious of your breath, taking time out from your busy schedule gives you the opportunity to recalibrate your system and reconnect with a deeper sense of relaxation.

Choose a day over the weekend when you're not beset with chores or social engagements, and set the scene the night before so there's nothing to distract you. Clearing any clutter from the rooms you'll be meditating in will create a calming atmosphere, while changing your bedding and having a bath or shower the night before will help you wake with a sense of optimism – a reminder that every breath is, in fact, a new beginning. Leaf through this book to use any of the practices and meditations you are drawn to, and find more inspiration over the following pages. Mindfulness is about listening to your body and responding to your needs moment by moment, so follow your instinct and choose only those that speak to your heart.

1 START THE DAY ON A MINDFUL NOTE

Even before you get out of bed, check in with how you're feeling. Lie on your back and bring your attention to the area below your navel. From there, tune in to how your body is feeling on a physical level. Do you notice any areas of stiffness or tension? Spend time opening yourself to the sensations you are experiencing.

Next, move your awareness to your heart area and ask yourself how you're feeling emotionally. Finally, rest your attention on a point mid-way between your eyebrows and spend a couple of moments observing your thoughts. When you're ready, take a few deep breaths into your belly, have a good stretch and begin your day, accepting everything you're feeling in a non-judgemental way, and knowing that you are always enough.

2 CLARIFY YOUR NEEDS

Setting an intention is a surprisingly powerful way to focus your thoughts and tune in to what really matters to you. We use only a small proportion of our minds, as shown in the experiment where, using just the power of meditation, a group of monks generated enough body heat to dry wet sheets that had been placed on them while they were in a chilly room!

To find a meaningful intention for the day, gently close your eyes and take a couple of deep breaths, releasing any tension in your body as you exhale. After a few moments, allow your attention to sink into your lower belly and imagine you're breathing in and out of a 'hole' a couple of inches below your navel. When you've established this pattern, spend some time reflecting on what it is you most need today. Perhaps it's to rest deeply, or calm an overactive mind. When it becomes clear what will most support your mindful day, write it down in a positive way, perhaps in your mindfulness journal. For example, 'When I find myself overwhelmed by thinking, I will acknowledge my thoughts, thank them for trying to help me, then tell them "Today I need to rest, I will attend to you tomorrow".'

3 FEED YOUR BODY AND SOUL

It's hard to maintain a fresh and mindful state if your system is sluggish from too many high-fat, or sugar-rich foods. Today, make a conscious decision to eat in a way that feeds your body *and* your soul. This green breakfast bowl (see panel opposite) from *The Yoga Kitchen*, by Kimberly Parsons (Quadrille, £20), is healthy and filling, and nourishes your heart chakra which, as Parsons points out, 'is where we discover our true selves'. You can also use the suggestions on p90 to help you stay in a mindful contact with yourself as you cook and eat your meals today.

GREEN
BREAKFAST BOWL

Sauté one chopped garlic clove
in coconut oil, then add 10g
each of almonds, pumpkin
seeds and sunflower seeds and
toast until lightly browned. Stir
in 50g cooked quinoa, a little
sea salt, 25g spinach and 75g
chopped kale and cook until
slightly wilted, then remove
from the heat and spoon into
your favourite serving bowl.
Crumble 60g halloumi cheese
into the same pan, gently cook
until golden, then add to your
bowl along with a boiled egg,
cut in half, 25g sliced coconut,
a wedge of lemon and a
quarter of an avocado.

4 GIVE YOURSELF A MASSAGE

Massage is a wonderful way to tune into your body and practice self-care. You can make it even more therapeutic by focusing on acupuncture points that will enhance your energy and give you a more mindful sense of being present. Acupuncturist Cary Chester suggests using the following sequence to help you deeply relax and rebalance your mind and body (see Energise your system, below).

'Most of the acupressure points in this sequence will feel quite tender, so they'll be easy for you to locate,' says Chester. 'To treat yourself, press your thumb into the area and gently massage it until your instinct tells you to move on to the next point. Start on the left hand side of your body and work your way down to your foot, then swap sides and travel back up your right side. Working with these points will leave you re-energised, with a greater clarity of mind and a renewed sense of calm. Afterwards, lie on your back with your arms at your sides and your palms facing upwards to absorb the effects of the mini-treatment.'

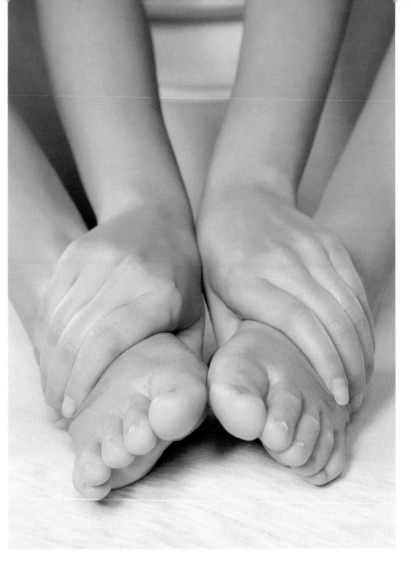

ENERGISE YOUR SYSTEM
Use these acupressure points to give yourself an uplifting massage

Hands
Locate the muscular web of skin between your thumb and index finger, and, using the thumb and index finger of your other hand, apply firm pressure to massage the area with tiny circles. Known as the Joining Valley, this point helps to calm a busy mind. Don't do this if you're pregnant.

Arms
Fold your forearm against your upper arm to create a crease at your elbow. With the base of your palm on your forearm and your fingers encircling your elbow, massage the point at the far end of the crease. You can apply deep pressure here, but use your intuition to guide you. This point is called Pool at the Crook, and is the main point for balancing the energy of your entire body.

Ankles
Measure three finger-widths above your inner ankle bone to find the Three Yin Intersection, a point where three meridians meet. You may find a slight hollow there and it's likely to feel tender if you press it firmly. Massage the area with small circles to tone your system and boost your energy. It's a particularly useful point for women, but do not use during pregnancy.

Feet
The last point, Great Surge, can be found a finger-distance away from the web of flesh between the first and second toe. Massaging this calming point has been scientifically shown to reduce anxiety, and boosts concentration and clarity of thought. It's also a major point for balancing the energy in your lower body. Mindfully massage the area with small circles.

5 SING TO YOURSELF

Softly singing or chanting opens up a whole world of healing potential. It comes from the devotional yoga tradition known as kirtan, and uses centuries' old Sanskrit words which carry a unique power that can calm, rebalance and transform your emotions, bringing you to a sense of peace with yourself. Rather than thinking of it as chanting to a specific deity or god, kirtan singer Krishna Das describes 'god' as an 'endless ocean of love, truth and presence', adding that when we see our own beauty, we understand that we are all connected.

If you haven't tried chanting before, *Invocation* with Ty Burhoe and Krishna Das (Tala Records, about £13), is a beautiful compilation of chants using the mantra 'Om Namah Shivaya Gurave', which translates as 'I bow to the goodness within myself'. The CD includes the words in Sanskrit and English, so you can easily join in. If you prefer not to, you can simply bathe in the sweetness of the melodies and still receive many of the benefits.

6 CLEANSE THE AIR

Add a few drops of frankincense essential oil to a burner to help create a meditative atmosphere. Frankincense has a sweet and spicy resinous odour, and has been used to enhance meditation for centuries. It's ideal for those times when you feel overwhelmed by the practicalities of life and have little time to connect to your deeper emotional or spiritual needs. If you feel trapped by mental clutter, frankincense will being a sense of calm to your life. Frankincense Essential Oil, £14,40 for 10ml, nealsyardremedies.com.

POCKET
mindfulness

With the help of these activities you'll be able to stay present throughout your day

*U*nlike formal mindfulness meditations, such as the body scan (p46) or mindful walking exercise (p66) in which you set aside a specific time to focus on a specific technique in isolation, when you practise informal mindfulness, you're bringing your attention to your mind, body or emotions from moment to moment throughout the course of the day. Becoming aware of your breath when you feel stressed at work, for example, can help dissipate the emotion in situ and bring you greater clarity of mind. Using visual reminders, such as the colour red, to anchor you in the present will lessen the possibility of becoming lost in your thoughts. Both forms of mindfulness are equally important. In fact, they feed each other, as practising in an informal way gives you the chance to practise and integrate the skills you're developing in longer meditations.

The following activities only take 10 minutes or less to complete. Work in a way and at a pace that suits you. You could choose one a day for 23 days or focus on the same theme for a few days and observe how your experiences deepen. It may take time to feel comfortable and confident with these exercises, so view them as a journey of discovery, without expectation or judgement. That way you're more likely to enjoy – and be present – for each step.

ACTIVITIES

On your own

With friends

At work

On the go

MINI MEDITATIONS

Feel your emotions

Sense your body

Still your mind

BEWARE OF TIME TRAVEL

This one may require a little practice. When you're talking to a friend and you notice yourself reacting, try to be aware if you're responding to what is happening in the present, or if something in the past is fuelling your reaction. Perhaps she was an hour late for a movie once and you missed the screening; this time she may just have been 10 minutes late but it's made you livid. It's not unusual to hold onto past experiences and react to them in the present. When something irks you, pause, take a breath and tune into your centre and see if you've been in the same situation before. From this awareness, you can decide how you want to respond.

GET STRESS AWARE

Observe what it is that makes you riled at the office. A particular person not pulling their weight, excessive talking when you have a deadline to meet, the manager who never notices how much overtime you do. Notice the effect on your body and breathe. It's much easier to decide how you want to respond when you're feeling calm.

MEET YOURSELF

Spend some time each day alone – even if it's just five minutes. Turn off the TV, put your mobile on silent and just be with yourself. Allow whatever you're thinking or feeling to come to the foreground and simply breathe it in. When we first practise mindfulness, it's often easier to become aware of being in the now if we minimise our distractions.

Be present

When speaking to a friend or colleague, give them your undivided attention. Focus on what they're saying and not what's happening around you. Resist the urge to interrupt or give your opinion – listen wholeheartedly. Not only will they feel deeply heard, it also brings you, the listener, a wonderful experience of feeling grounded and fully present.

KEEP A JOURNAL

Keeping track of your mindfulness experiences will give you the opportunity to record and reflect on what you've experienced during the day. You can use it to keep track of your intentions, to notice any patterns that are emerging and to highlight any areas you want to revisit and work on more deeply.

ARE YOU JUDGING OTHERS?

When speaking to or about a friend or family member, be aware of any negative thoughts you have about them. Are you mentally judging their clothing, their behaviour or their drinking habits? Often, we dislike things in others that we haven't yet accepted about ourselves. And remember, this is just an exercise in awareness, so be careful not to judge yourself about the thoughts that you're having!

DO SOMETHING DIFFERENT

When you're out and about, try breaking out of your routine. Travel by bus instead of train, go to a different supermarket, visit a place you've never been to before. Any time you catch yourself falling into a familiar pattern, ask yourself if you could do it differently. Surprising your mind will wake it up and introduce new experiences for it to engage with in the here and now.

Have a heart

Take your attention to your heart area and ask yourself what you are experiencing emotionally at this moment. Give yourself a minute or two for your feelings to register. Are there any physical sensations? A racing pulse? A gentle ache? A tingling sense of excitement? You don't need to try to change anything, just notice. Often we cut off from how we feel to get through the task at hand, but by bringing your emotions more into your awareness you can be a little kinder to yourself throughout the day.

BE A CHILD AGAIN

Set aside an hour or two (or a day if you're on holiday) and indulge your inner child. Take her to an art gallery or an afternoon movie, let her eat whatever she fancies or give her permission to run barefoot on the grass/sand with no fitness agenda whatsoever! Ask her what she would really like to do if everything was allowed, and then let her with no judgements and no limitations. Then see how you feel afterwards.

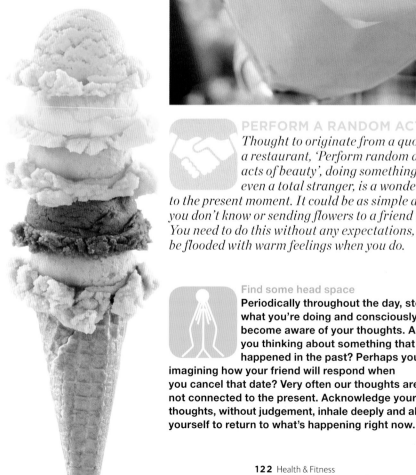

PERFORM A RANDOM ACT OF KINDNESS

Thought to originate from a quote written on a place mat at a restaurant, 'Perform random acts of kindness and senseless acts of beauty', doing something unexpected for a friend or even a total stranger, is a wonderful way to wake you both up to the present moment. It could be as simple as smiling warmly at someone you don't know or sending flowers to a friend who's been feeling down. You need to do this without any expectations, but the likelihood is you'll be flooded with warm feelings when you do.

Find some head space

Periodically throughout the day, stop what you're doing and consciously become aware of your thoughts. Are you thinking about something that happened in the past? Perhaps you're imagining how your friend will respond when you cancel that date? Very often our thoughts are not connected to the present. Acknowledge your thoughts, without judgement, inhale deeply and allow yourself to return to what's happening right now.

BE YOUR OWN BEST FRIEND

Do you feel better about yourself when you achieve a goal, but criticise yourself if you don't? Rather than place value judgements on yourself, today see if you can cultivate an attitude of observation instead, so you become more aware of these inner dialogues. Notice what stories accompany your behaviour. 'I must do better.' 'If I was more thoughtful I would have acted differently.' If it helps, when you see a judgemental thought arise, label it 'thinking', and take your attention to your breath for a couple of moments.

Take a sound bath

Spend some time focusing on the sounds around you. A humming fridge, the sound of traffic or noisy conversation in a café. If you're in a relatively quiet place, see if you can tune into the sounds outside your building. Then bring your attention closer and focus on any sounds inside the room. If you can, go even deeper and listen to the sound of your own body. A rumbling tummy or the sound of your breath, perhaps. Even if you don't like what you're hearing, just allow the sound to exit, and see if that changes how you feel about it.

Monotask!

Forget doing three things at once, choose a single activity and complete it before moving onto the next. Don't just give it your full attention, but also carry out the job in minute detail. It's an interesting exercise to do this with something you don't usually enjoy. If you choose washing the dishes, for example, look carefully at each piece of crockery you clean. Are there areas you sometimes miss, such as the back of a plate or the outside of the frying pan? This time, give those areas extra attention and make them sparkle. If you normally let the dishes drain, try drying them, packing them away, then drying beneath the draining rack. Notice how it feels to completely absorb yourself in an activity from the beginning right through to the end.

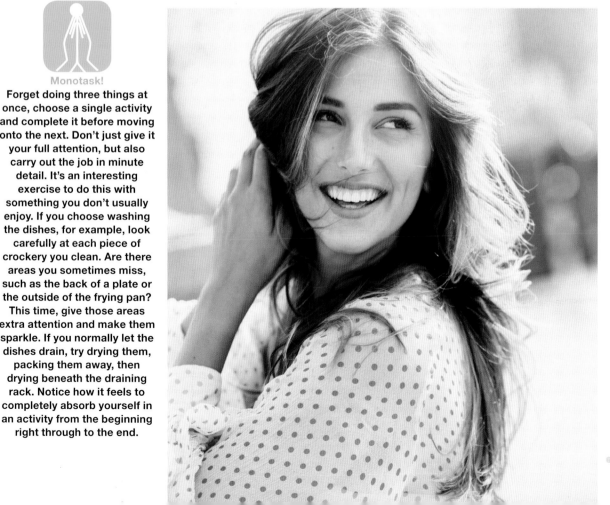

See red

Vietnamese monk, Thich Naht Hahn, suggests pausing and turning your attention inwards each time you see a red traffic light. If you extend this to every time you see the colour red, it's a useful reminder to pause for a moment to deepen your breathing, become aware of any unnecessary tension you're holding and to come back to the present moment, sensing what is real for you right now.

BE A ROOKIE

Take on a task you've never done before. Mentor a new member of staff, learn a piece of software or offer to help out a colleague who's feeling under pressure. With a beginner's mind, you'll see things with fresh eyes – you really have to be in the moment when you learn something new – and you're more likely to accept that you don't have to be perfect.

Feel your feet

When you're waiting for a train or queuing at a checkout, rather than feel frustrated or anxious, allow your attention to drop into your feet. Feel the point of contact between your soles and the ground. Imagine your breath travelling from your sacrum down both your legs and out through your feet into the ground. Notice how this simple grounding practice affects your whole body.

BE GRATEFUL

There is a lot of talk about gratitude journals these days, but instead of recalling three things you're grateful for at the end of the day, see if you can fully appreciate positive experiences in the moment. Be aware of your thoughts, feelings and bodily sensations at the time. Rather than rush into the next activity in your day, take a moment or two to appreciate them fully. Take a deep breath in and allow them to expand until they fill your experience.

GET CLEAR

Setting an intention for the day is a valuable way to give focus to your mindfulness journey. Perhaps you want to work on connecting to your breath when you feel stressed, or maybe you'd like to tune into your senses to help calm a busy mind. By singling out an area to give your attention to, you create a point of reference to return to throughout the day. To set an intention, sit quietly for a few breaths to create a state of restful awareness, then take your attention to the area below your navel and ask yourself 'What do I need for today?' Trust the first answer that comes to you and make that the focus of your day.

Posture play

Without trying to change anything, tune into your body and notice how you are sitting, standing or lying. Are you leaning on one leg more than the other? Is your neck jutting forwards? Are your shoulders hunched? Notice if you're holding your breath as well as your muscles. It's hard to be fully present in the moment if you're tensing your body. Simply becoming aware of the tension may allow you to let it go.

ACT AS IF...

As an experiment, the next time you have a task you really don't feel like doing, imagine it's the most important thing you've ever been asked to do, perhaps a piece of work that will lead to your dream job. Give it all your attention and care, and notice if this changes your feelings about doing it.

Smile inside

Practise smiling on the inside. Simply imagine you're smiling and notice the difference it makes. How does your face feel? How does your heart feel? What do you notice about the area around you? Your experience in the here and now is not fixed, but dependent on your relationship to it. Experiment for yourself and see what you notice.

Directory

✳ EQUIPMENT

kikki.K
kikki-k.com

Yoga Matters
yogamatters.com

Neom Organics
neomorganics.com

Neal's Yard Remedies
nealsyardremedies.com

Ty Burhoe & Tala Records
tyburhoe.com

✳ TEACHERS & CENTRES

Be Mindful
bemindful.co.uk

Harley Therapy
harleytherapy.co.uk

Jack Kornfield
jackkornfield.com

Tara Brach
tarabrach.com

Sharon Salzberg
sharonsalzberg.com

George Langenberg
georgelangenberg.com

London Meditation Centre
londonmeditationcentre.com

Ashvin Omkar Patel
holisticomkar.com

Belinda Freeman
mindfulmind.co.uk

Tessa Watt
beingmindful.co.uk

AJ Bicât
ajbicat.com

Nicole Perkins
nicoleperkinsmindfulness.com

Uz Afzal
beherebreathe.co.uk

Rosalie Dores
optimalliving.co.uk

✳ APPS

Insight Timer
insighttimer.com

Aura
aurahealth.io

Ekhart Yoga
ekhartyoga.com

✳ BOOKS

The Miracle of Mindfulness, Thich Nhat Hanh (Rider, £7.99)

Where You Go, There You Are, Jon Kabat-Zinn (Piatkus, £13.99)

Bringing Home the Dharma: Awakening Right Where You Are, Jack Kornfield (Shambhala Publications Inc, £13.10)

The Breathing Book: Vitality and Good Health through Essential Breath Work, Donna Farhi (Henry Holt & Co, £15.99)

Real Happiness: The Power of Meditation, Sharon Salzburg (Hay House, £12.99)

Radical Acceptance: Embracing Your Life With the Heart of a Buddha, Tara Brach (Bantam, £8.62)

Mindfulness and Performance, Amy L. Baltzell (Cambridge University Press, £29.99)

Mindfulness: Be mindful. Live in the moment, Gill Hasson (Capstone, £10.99)

Mind, Body & Soul

FOUR WEEK BIKINI BODY!

Your complete guide to getting lean fast!

+ Easy-to-follow plan for all ability levels

+ Burn off body fat and sculpt toned muscles

+ Expert food and habit advice for a leaner body

GYM FREE PLAN!

Complete guide to toning up your body in just four weeks. Following a simple step-by-step programme, you'll burn more fat and develop lean, defined muscles. Plus, learn good habits that will make you healthier for life.

Spring 2019 – Available to pre-order

QUICK FIX FAT LOSS

Your 8-week guide to burning body fat and building muscle

This new eight-week training and eating plan that will help you shift body fat fast and allow you to build the body you've always wanted. In many ways you've already done the hardest part of any fat loss journey: you've bought this book and proved you are ready to make a commitment to improve your health and build a leaner, fitter body.

Spring 2019 – Available to pre-order

Mind, Body & Soul

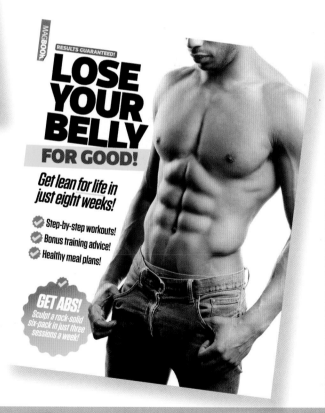

✳

Congratulations on completing this stage of your mindfulness journey. Hopefully, becoming more familiar with the techniques and meditation practices in this book will have given you a taste of some of the ways being more mindful can help you ease stress, find beauty in each moment and live a fuller, richer life. Many of the practices have been shown to aid sleep, ease pain and help you become a happier, calmer person – and the more you work with them, the more benefits you'll experience. This is just the beginning!

And finally, remember, whatever else is happening in your life, make space to connect to your breath, the anchor that helps you return to yourself with soft acceptance. In the same way that, over time, even a trickle of water can erode the hardest of rocks, being gently connected to your breath and the present moment is a source of unimaginable inner strength.

I wish you well.